Margaret Worthington (?)

Bear With Me
Tales From
FURNACE BROOK FARM

by Margaret M. Waddington

D1534620

Academy Books

Other publications by the author:

Atlas of Cerebral Angiography with Anatomic Correlation
Atlas of the Human Skull
Atlas of Human Intracranial Anatomy

The Little C. Lions	Reading Between the Lions
Caterpillar to Butterfly	Lion Winter Games
A Glimpse of Big Sky	Vignettes from Life
Nothing is Forever	Corporate Lions
Enchanted Weekend	Bearly A Lion
The Waiting Room	A Glimpse of Vermont
Memorable Events	Teddy Bear's Memoirs

The Lions' Observations & Opinions
Furnace Brook Farm
The Story of OUR BEAR
Four Seasons at Furnace Brook Farm
Wild Oats at Furnace Brook Farm

Illustrations by the author:

The First Colored Easter Eggs
The Saga of Nifty Snifty
Boyhood Memories

Cover photo:
The Monarch – Vermont State Butterfly

For additional copies of this book, write to:
ACADEMY BOOKS
P.O. 757 · 10 Cleveland Avenue · Rutland, Vermont 05702

ii

Dedicated to

the one who said,

"Margaret, Margaret,

please bring me my tiger."

Dare to Risk

To laugh is to risk appearing the fool.
To weep is to risk appearing sentimental.
To reach for another is to risk involvement.
To expose your ideas, your dreams, before a
    crowd is to risk their loss.
To love is to risk being loved in return.
But risks must be taken, because the
    greatest hazard in life is to risk nothing.
The people who risk nothing, do nothing,
    have nothing, are nothing.
They may avoid suffering, and sorrow, but
    they cannot learn, feel, change, grow,
    love, live.
Chained by their attitudes, they are slaves;
    they have forefeited their freedom.
Only a person who risks is free.

–Author Unknown

Author's Note

In this book you will read about thought equivalents and stuffed equivalents, about barely a thought and bear thoughts, and even about a Siberian tiger in Vermont!

So . . . bear with me and enjoy the *whimsy* . . . the capricious or eccentric and often sudden idea or turn of mind.

The animal photography was done at Mountain Top Inn in Chittenden, Vermont, during the 1996 fall wildlife photography workshop. The Siberian tiger and the other animals were brought in by the Triple "D" Game Farm of Kalispell, Montana. The sponsors for the workshop were Canon, Hasselblad University, Kodak, and MWM Dexter Inc. The wildlife photographer who organized the workshop was Judy Holmes from Jackson, New Hampshire. Although not a professional, I was privileged to attend the session.

My editor, Kathy Carrara, patiently corrected the manuscript, and Academy Press, true to their tradition, spared no effort in turning out a handsome book.

Friends who listened to the stories came up with suggestions and much laughter. This gave me the courage to go on. To all, my gratitude and thanks.

Table of Contents

Green Mountain Bear.

What Is That Strange Sound?

June 15, 1996

Today I finished the manuscript for my third book of a series, *Wild Oats at Furnace Brook Farm*. Monday morning I'll turn in the manuscript to my publisher. Exuberant at this accomplishment, and feeling well with the privilege of quiet and solitude, I settle at my nicely tuned piano to indulge in the fun of making music, returning to J. S. Bach for the special place his music holds for me.

While engaged in working out a new passage, I hear next to me a louder-than-usual tapping on the window. Could it be Green Mountain Bear? I suppose I'll have to give the bear a moment of my time. He must have some concern to drop by on this pleasant summer evening.

"You are not supposed to interrupt a musician!" I admonish my friend as I open the window. "This is not the window you usually come to; I expect you at the one in the den. So, tell me, what is troubling you?"

"I'm not troubled, really. While I was moseying about, I heard strange sounds coming from the house and I decided to investigate."

"What do you mean *strange* sounds?" I inquire.

"I do not hear them now," he replies.

I proceed to play a chord on the piano with my right hand.

"There—that's it—the strange sound. Can't you hear it?" the bear responds all excited.

1

"That sound happens to come from a beautiful musical instrument called a piano," I explain.

"Do you play it well, or are you out of practice?" the bear asks as inquisitive as always.

"Out of practice? Why, always! And if you have a good ear and excellent rhythm, as is common among bears, you'll probably head right back up to the top of your mountain and hide in the den and plug your ears."

"Oh, your playing is not that bad! I enjoy piano sound and melody. Except, sometimes you repeat the same music over and over again, then I get impatient."

"That is called practicing, and I have to practice a great deal. I'm not good at sight reading and I do not even claim to be a musician. I just love the sound of music, and you caught me having a very good private time. My piano playing is not intended for anyone's ears other than my own—not even for a bear's."

"Isn't this very selfish?" the bear inquires.

"No, not really. There are times in life when doing something just for the pleasure is enough reason to just do it. I prefer not to have an audience because then I can enjoy the music without feeling self conscious."

"Am I considered audience? I hope not. For I find the sound of the piano enjoyable and will come to listen, even if you do not like it. I can sneak up quietly and you'll never even know I'm here."

2

"You rascal! Would you really pull that on me?"

"How else will I get to listen to piano sound?"

"You should drop by when Louise plays on the instrument—then you will hear real music beautifully executed. She taught me all I know about playing the piano. Louise is an angel to have given so much of her time to one so untalented."

"Never mind. I like your playing well enough," the bear says as though to console me.

"Now that my manuscript is finished, you may hear me practice more often, and maybe I'll improve over time."

"So, may I be your audience? And may I bring other animals?"

"No, that is going too far. You are driving a hard bargain again," I reply sternly.

"More than one animal would give much more applause than I can make with my two paws. Does not everyone like applause?"

"I told you my music is a private affair!"

"Is that really fun for you? Are you happy playing piano sounds?"

"Yes, I'm quite happy playing. Otherwise I'd do something else, like read a book. Therefore, if you have nothing else on your mind, I'd like to get back to the piano. Interruptions do not help, whether it is the phone or you, my friend. So, I think it is time for you to be on your way. Good evening, and off you trot."

3

The woods at Furnace Brook Farm.

The waterfall at the farm.

"I'll see you soon. Good evening and good hunting. One of these days, I'll catch a fish."

"Good, but please do not come to show off the dead fish. I know you are capable of this. You might want some approval and applause, which I'll give you without the need to present the evidence."

"Okay, I'm on my way! You seem less than patient with me this evening. I suppose you want to get back to making piano sounds."

"Precisely. We'll talk some more another time."

I close the window and watch the bear head towards the woods slowly and pensively. I think he is listening for more "piano sounds," as he calls my performance. Funny little fellow! I really don't mind his interruptions all that much. Maybe now I will put more effort into playing according to the way Bach wrote the music. The bear, more likely than not, will comment when he comes again. If only he leaves all the other animals in the woods. I don't need any audience— not even that of wild animals.

My attention returns to the piano. Time flies. Soon it is bedtime even for the one who enjoys making "piano sounds." This has been a happy ending to a delightful day.

Summer Solstice

June 20, 1996

This is a sad day in my calendar of life. I feel disappointment as the days will become shorter and fall and winter are on their way so soon again. The foliage of the trees is a succulent dark green. This year we are getting ample amounts of rain. We are lucky to have two sunny days a week. Just time enough to mow the lush grass rich in clover.

How nice, I can see Green Mountain Bear coming down to the farm. He is cautiously approaching the den window.

"Do you mind if I take a bit of your time this evening?" the bear inquires.

"Why, of course not! I am not making piano sounds. I've been at the computer as you suspected, even though the window is only partially open."

We both seem glad for each other's company.

"Little bear, your eyes look inflamed. What has happened to you?" I am concerned to see the white of the bear's eyes red and infected.

"Little flies, horse flies, or deer flies—whatever you want to call them—are a real pest this summer. I've had several lodge in my eyes and it makes me so uncomfortable. Can you help me please?" the bear asks in a pleading, nearly pathetic voice. "You were able to help Mountain Lion . . . maybe you can help me."

I look over Green Mountain Bear's face. His nose is swollen and bleeding from too much scratching. "Your nose is quite uncomfortable too, I suspect."

"Oh, yes, the mosquitoes just won't let up in the woods, and along the brook they plague me."

"Well, I think if you can hold your head quiet and not move, I'll get my bottle of natural tears and wash out your eyes first. I can see several dead horse flies in each eye. No wonder you are miserable!"

"I'll keep very quiet. Don't worry. I know you will be gentle; you were with Mountain Lion last November, and he was in worse shape than I am this evening."

The bear is still resting his head on the den windowsill by the time I return.

"Okay, now look up. I'll turn down your lower lid and you will feel the cool eye drops wash over the eye. Just don't jerk your head, please. I do not wish to scratch your cornea. It would make matters worse."

"Oh, this feels good and refreshing. The scratching has let up. Thanks! Please don't forget my other eye."

"Not likely. It is the same procedure. Look up and hold still," I instruct my four-legged patient.

"Am I doing things right?" the bear inquires.

"Sure. Don't your eyes feel much better now?"

"Yes, very much more comfortable. Most of the day I was miserable."

"Now I believe I may be able to help you a little with your nose. I'll wash it well with warm salt water and then apply to your fur a good dose of insect repellent. You will be more comfortable in a short while."

"Ooooh, the insect repellent burns on my nose," the bear moans. "May I open my eyes now?" the bear pleads.

"Sure, we are just about finished."

"Last year Mother attended to me and my brother and licked our tender noses and took us to the brook to wash out our sore eyes. I miss my mother and brother," the little bear reminisces.

Red clover, the Vermont State flower.

"I know," I reply consolingly, "I can only be a so-so substitute . . . though better than no one."

"Will you give me a dish of milk and honey now? I did not find many grubs today."

"Come on, you're quite alright now. Don't fall into a fit of feeling sorry for yourself!" I would love to spoil this bear, though I know I must refrain. "Have you noticed the blackberries are in full bloom and we may have a wonderful harvest if all goes well? You'll enjoy that, won't you?"

"Yes, I like blackberries, though they have more thorns than the raspberries," he replies.

"If you get a thorn in your nose or your paws, just drop by and I'll remove the thorn," I instruct.

"Thanks, that is real nice of you. Now I think I'll return to my den for a good night's sleep. I'm weary this evening."

"I know what you are telling me. I too am weary on some evenings. Then you will hear no piano sounds."

"Maybe tomorrow?" the bear asks.

"Maybe tomorrow," I agree. "If your eyes bother you, come back and I will rinse them again. Natural tears are harmless and quite refreshing."

"Thanks, I'll remember this."

Before I can add to the conversation, the bear scampers off into the woods. I never thought my medical experience would serve the animals so well. Glad I have a little background and can help on occasion.

Shakespeare's Flowers at the Farm

June 26, 1996

This writing is based on the book, *Shakespeare's Flowers,* by Jessica Kerr, printed in Belgium in 1969. The book was one of my mother's favorites. Only recently did I take time to pick it up and spend some time enjoying the flowers of 400 years ago. Then when I came upon the reference to burdock as a crown for King Lear I decided to see how many weeds or flowers in Shakespeare's time can be found at the farm.

Here is a list:

Burdock · Columbine · Crabapple

Daffodils · Daisies · Fennel

Flower-de-luce (Florentine iris and wild iris fleur de lys, as it has come to be called)

Hemlock · Lily · Marigold

Mint (curly and spear) · Nettles

Pansy (known as Johnny Jump-Up)

Rose (red and white)

Azured Harbell (Cymbeline)
(called wild hyacinth today)

Thyme · Violets (blue) · Wild Marjoram

Woodbine (wild honeysuckle)

Some of Shakespeare's flowers do not grow in New England. Others do, though not on this farm. Then, too, there are flowers common to New England growing on this farm that are not mentioned by Shakespeare:

11

Wild Oats
Trillium (red predominantly)
Trout lily
Marsh marigold
Several small 5-to-6-petaled white flowers
Peonies
Trumpet Vine
Lilac bushes
Sunflowers
Black-eyed Susan
Dutchman's-Breeches
and several others.

Burdock made a crown for King Lear.

Columbine, a long-time survivor.

A Dark Figure at the Den Window

June 28, 1996

Last evening I had supper with Katherine at her home about a mile south of the farm. It was most pleasant. We shared ideas, memories, and a delicious meal. When I departed for the farm it was near dusk. As I drove into the driveway I noticed a dark figure near my den window. So, Green Mountain Bear has come calling. He surely will express consternation that I'm not at the computer by this time of day.

Momentarily I reach the den and put on the light, I find the window is wide open and the bear is leaning on the windowsill in expectation of my arrival—or maybe just exploring the inside of the room.

"Welcome home!" the bear greets me. "Where have you been this evening?" the bear asks in his usual curious frame of mind.

"Is it any of your business?" I inquire.

"It might be . . . if you were lost or in trouble."

"Would the blue jays inform you? It seems to me I'm losing some of my privacy and freedom to the animal kingdom."

"I like to know what is going on and that those I care about are safe and sound," the bear responds.

"No need to worry," I reassure the bear.

What about the other day when you crossed the brook wearing your red boots, jeans, and a pink shirt, and you had your camera slung around your

14

neck? You nearly lost your balance and might have ruined your good camera in the process. Katherine saw you and came to your rescue when you were stranded. By then you realized the stones were slippery and the current was quite swift. Did you hear the jays squawk? In no time I knew all about this incident. Katherine held out to you a long sapling which she cut off in a hurry. She rescued you and all you did was giggle and laugh. What was so funny about this stupidity?"

"I don't owe you, or anyone else for that matter, any explanation. Sometimes in life one gets a yen to be young again. It was a perfect summer day and I was tired from climbing around in the woods. It seemed like a delightful opportunity to cool off, get across the brook by a shortcut, and enjoy the experience at the same time. I knew I had no business attempting the crossing, especially putting the camera at risk. At that moment the camera wasn't foremost on my mind. I had fun—lots of fun—and Katherine also laughed when she realized the bright pink blob in the brook was a well known human being who sometimes did odd things. So does that satisfy your curiosity?"

"To tell you the truth, I laughed when I heard the story and wished I had your camera so I could have taken some photos. It was fortunate that the day was warm and lunchtime was nearing. You were rather wet, I'm told."

"Rather wet, but that is irrelevant. It was fun and that's what mattered. I can imagine what you would have thought had I slipped and landed in the brook and got soaked from top to bottom."

"I would have come to your rescue. Now you know why I worry some about your antics!"

"As you grow up this will be less of a problem. You can't go through life worrying too much," I warn.

"How can one tell if it is 'too much'?" the bear pursues the question further.

"'Too much' happens when worry interferes with taking risks, having good fun, and when laughter stops. Laughter is an important ingredient of life."

"Who taught you this?"

"I can't remember," I reply. "It may have been during wartime. Laughter stopped and life became sad and dreary."

"Wartime is when humans kill humans, isn't it? Bears do not engage in war as far as I know. They are smart, aren't they?" he exclaims.

"Oh, very smart, and curious, in case you don't know," I respond reassuringly.

"You have told me as much, more than once."

"Now, what have you been up to?" I ask my friend.

"I've been enjoying the first wild strawberries. They are large and sweet this year," the bear announces.

"It is the rain we've had that has helped the fruit to be lush," I explain. "By the way, Katherine has a message for you."

16

"What's that?" the bear inquires.

"Katherine wants you to know that some of the largest strawberries are in the north field near the woods and the road. Just be careful crossing the road at all times. The deer just dash into the road without thought or hesitation. Then, too, a Rottweiler puppy down the road can be a fierce attacker. This dog will grow to be tall and strong, even able to tackle a bear," I warn.

"Thanks for the message and caution which you express. Are you a little worried about me right now?"

"Probably, it is only human to worry about a loved one."

"Well, finally, maybe now you are getting to the point. I thought this was self-evident."

"Don't get too smart, little bear!"

"I'm glad we had this discussion. I think I may have learned a thing or two. Thanks! And I'll see you soon."

With this having been said, the bear heads off for the woods.

What Happened?

July 7, 1996

"Green Mountain Bear, what brings you calling this evening?" I inquire of my friend when I hear him in the lilac bush next to the homestead.

"I've come to find out what really happened. The jays came to tell me you were of great help to them in avoiding a near-tragedy. They were so out of breath and so upset I could not make head or tail of their story. They were all squawking at once. It is hard enough to understand one at a time."

"So, you must be anxious to know what happened at noon today."

"Yes, yes, it is something that happened at the farm about midday—it is a time when there is usually peace and quiet—your lunchtime."

"I'll tell you. I was waiting for friends and sitting on the porch enjoying the sunshine and the beauty of some of my roses."

"That is not important," the bear comments. He is as impatient and as curious as always.

"Now don't you interrupt my story. I was just giving you the lead-in."

"Not essential, not essential! I'm in a hurry this evening. I have to go after some of the ripe wild strawberries before others clean them all up."

"Now, then, while I was enjoying the beauty of the day I hear loud squawking from more than one bird. Something is upsetting the birds—but what? Soon I find out. A red-tailed hawk is below the large apple tree with a small bird in his claws. Two robins are dive-bombing the hawk with no result. The small bird is firmly in the grip of the hawk. Then three jays arrive and join the robins who are flying fearlessly at the predator. The hawk moves a few feet but won't release the bird. Then two male rose-breasted grosbeaks join the fray. Now the hawk flies toward the woods. The small birds all follow. From where I am standing I clap my hands. This startles the hawk and he releases the captured bird. The young robin flies about fifty feet and settles in the field. I pursue the hawk. With the help of the seven small birds, we finally drive off the hawk. The big bird flies south. The seven temporary friends part ways. The squawking lets up. Then I inspect the young robin, victim of the hawk. The bird is panting and totally exhausted, though still on its feet. I take a ten-minute walk and return to see if this is a suffering animal which I may need to put out of its misery. The panting has let up. When the robin sights me it flies about twenty feet into thick, uncut grass. I'm delighted, for there it will be much better hidden than on the mowed hayfield. Then I head home in time to receive my friends for lunch.

"Maybe the seven birds could have intimidated the hawk sufficiently to free the young robin. I was not sure, so I intervened in my own way. That is all there is to the story."

"No wonder the jays were upset," the little bear responds. "They did keep squawking about robins and grosbeaks. I could not make sense of their story. Thanks for helping my feathered friends. I know they appreciate your intervention. They had called all birds within reach. I'm surprised seven were unable to effectively accomplish the release of the young robin. I'm glad it looks as though the robin will be all right. If you don't mind, I'll be off now. I hunger for strawberries!"

Jim's Luck

July 10, 1996

Jim Moore tells this story with obvious delight:
"As you know, I have wanted an evaporator pan
to boil down maple sap. These pans are made in
Rutland and are incredibly expensive when
bought new because special metal is used in the
manufacturing process. I went to the company
and was told a second-hand pan in the size I need
is selling for $1,500—well beyond my means.

"Anyway, I went to my first auction in New York
State the other day with my wife Betsy who suggested we attend as there was an evaporator pan
advertised for sale. I hoped the used pan might
go for a lot less. I asked the auctioneer to put the
pan up for bid before midday, as Betsy had to be
at work by noon. At first he hesitated, but finally
the evaporator pan was put on the auction block.
'I have a bid for $25,' the auctioneer announced.
I was reluctant to bid since I hoped I could get the
pan for that price! Then Betsy urged me, 'Bid!
You never spend any money on things you want!'
The bidding was brief and I got the evaporator
pan for $250.

"Then the auctioneer offered 45 maple buckets
in excellent condition, adding that the taps were
in between the buckets. 'Hear them rattle,' he
announced as he shook the buckets to prove they
were in there. So, I bought the buckets for one
dollar a piece, as that was an excellent price."

Jim explains that he returned home with all his goods, pleased at the prospect of fine maple syrup next spring. "I love New York," crosses his mind, though in principle he is a real Vermonter and does not like to cross into another state.

That afternoon while exploring and washing the maple buckets, he finds two small golden rings and a small bag containing gold nuggets hidden between the buckets. That is what rattled when the buckets were shook! This certainly is an unexpected surprise. He takes the gold to a friend who deals in jewelry who estimates the value of the rings and gold nuggets to be $700! Not bad for a day at the auction.

Jim adds, "The buckets were a good hiding place for the valuables of this family. Who would ever think to look through used sap buckets for the jewels of the family? Then too, the person who makes his own maple syrup is probably a worthy recipient if there are no others to inherit the valuables."

Jim is content and Betsy is pleased she urged Jim to put in a bid. Is this a case of beginner's luck?

I've Returned!

Green Mountain Bear has been on his own for close to two weeks. When he announced, "Now I am on my way," and appeared to be in a big hurry, he really intended to tell me he was off into the national forest in search of a mate.

I'm wondering how he is making out especially the last two days when we had incredible fierce storms with thunder, wind, and sheets of pelting rain. Many trees in the forest have been uprooted. The waterfall by the homestead—one of his favorite spots at which to fish and bathe—has been blocked by two large trees which fell across the brook and impede access.

This evening it is mild and the window is open to welcome my friend perchance he is to come by. As dusk settles in, the jays start to announce a disturbance nearby. What is this all about? Before I have time to investigate, I hear rustling in the bushes by the house and then I perceive the dark outline of Green Mountain Bear.

"Hi . . . I've returned," the bear announces a bit sheepishly.

"Is that so? Welcome home, little fellow. I've missed your visits. Have you had a nice time?" I inquire.

"Oh, yes, it has been thrilling! And you will not believe my good luck."

"Good luck? What would that be?" I pursue his announcement, "Did you find your brother and mother?"

"No, they were nowhere in sight. I had much better luck than that."

"What could it have been?" I continue to heighten his delight by pretending utter ignorance.

"Guess what? I found the most beautiful, young female bear. You call her a sow, a term which I find quite unfitting and nearly insulting to a handsome young female bear. Bearess would sound nicer. You know lion/lioness . . . why not bear/bearess? In any event, she had large, dark eyes and slick, black fur. She is about my size, nearly three years old, and was she ever lonesome."

Green Mountain Bear continues, "She welcomed me and we had two delightful weeks of fun and games. My beloved showed me her den, which is really too small for two adult bears. It is just adequate for one her size. We ate wild black raspberries and blueberries. I was amazed. My mate knew exactly where they were growing and we got most of the ripe, sweet berries before the moose showed up. We drank from the springs that feed Furnace Brook. I caught several trout for my endearing companion. She enjoyed these treats. I am far more able to catch trout than she is. It is a skill she had not acquired from her mother, or so she professed. We chased each other up and down the mountain until both of us were exhausted. We were so enchanted that we had nothing but one another in mind. At night we remained close, in a warm embrace. It seemed like heaven to both of us. I quoted to her the *Maxims of Baloo*, which you passed on to me this spring, as well as many of the other lessons I learned from you. My beloved will need all this information next spring when she starts raising her young. We debated whether the cubs would

Wild black raspberries

resemble me or her. We laughed about this and many other subjects that came up," he muses.

The bear continues, "These were the most thrilling days of my life. But like all things in life these wonderful times had to come to an end. The fierce storms were disruptive and I became concerned about my den. I did not want any other bear to occupy my den. I'm in no mood for a territorial fight. So I took off one morning and . . . well . . . here I am. I think my lady friend will be happy to be rid of me. Maybe I was becoming a bit of a nuisance," he concedes.

"Next spring I plan to venture back into her territory to see my newborn sons or daughters. We had an argument about this matter. My mate was not sure I'd be welcome. She claimed the cubs were all her own to raise and enjoy. It sounded like a most selfish attitude. I was quite annoyed at her and told her so. This disagreement made parting easy. She claimed she would look for a new territory and that I would never locate the cubs. Seems like that's what happened in my family. I've never seen my dad. Maybe this is for the better, though I'm not convinced. What do you think?"

I explain, "Some dads get very jealous of their cubs and it is claimed they may kill their own. This is not true for every bear—you'd surely be the exception. Mother nature makes little allowance for individual differences. So the word is passed on from mother to daughter to take no chances with their cubs. By next spring you will be a large bear and your mate will be unable to defend the cubs successfully in the event were you to attack them in a fury of rage. You have always faithfully listened to the words of your mother, so you cannot and should not blame your friend for heeding what she was told while she was growing up. She knows she can find you at Furnace Brook Farm. You never can tell, she may bring the cubs to introduce them. I'd not fret about the matter until a year from now. Much water will flow over the dam before the cubs are born and grow big enough to come safely off the mountain for a visit. I would not be surprised if someday you'll arrive at the window with the entire family. Let mother come to you to show off the young. In the meantime, you have much catching up to do. As a matter of fact, you've lost much weight. You need to put on some girth and get in shape for a long winter. It is nice you're back. Here you have friends to make life quite pleasant. Good night, now, and I'll see you soon."

"Thanks for being so welcoming. I was beginning to feel quite sorry for myself," the bear admits.

"I know," I say consolingly. "Now, back up to your den before it starts to rain and storm again. We will have plenty of time to chat before you go into hibernation."

27

A Follow-up Report

July 28, 1996

Harlequin Bear and the ever-so-wise Hooty the Owl are delighted to have joined the gang of stuffed bears at Furnace Brook Farm.

Harlequin Bear tells me he escaped from the circus with the aid and advice from Hooty the Owl who is not saying much—he seems exhausted for the moment. But Harlequin Bear is a different story. He is tumbling and turning somersaults and garnering much recognition and attention from all the other bears. Masked Bear, with his background in circuses, is astounded at Harlequin Bear's versatility. Masked Bear can dance on his hind legs but that does not compare to the tumbling of Harlequin Bear.

During his escape from the circus Harlequin Bear lost his mask somewhere. Hooty the Owl told him not to spend time searching for his mask—too much precious time in their escape would be lost. He explained that although a mask is an integral part of Harlequin garb, getting away is most important!

I feel the farm will be good for these escapees. They will need a long time to get their sense of self-importance and courage. For the moment, I've not been given all the details of their life and background.

28

More Rain

August 1, 1996

The weather this year is a major contrast to the one just past. In July there was 13.1 inches more rain than average for the state. Last year we had a 7-inch shortfall. This is the wettest summer that I can recall in Vermont. It seems to me as if I'm spending the summer in Ireland. Daily heavy thunderstorms or rainstorms last all day long with only a few hours here and there to cut the grass before the next bout of precipitation.

Lush green fields.

Furnace Brook is positively noisy, running high and often carrying much earth. It is so wild we cannot contemplate cleaning the brook this year; the current is too swift. Maybe August and September will bring a change in the weather pattern—though I do not count on it. I'm glad all this water isn't arriving as snow, at least not yet.

Golf matches, which are a big deal in Vermont each summer, are being canceled as the land is too wet to walk on, never mind to drive over with the little golf carts.

Trees are uprooting and the woods are beginning to look messy. Presently six large trees are bridging Furnace Brook. One of these days Elmer will arrive with a bulldozer. He will attempt to pull the tree trunks out of the brook and then my neighbor, Rick LaPorte, will cut up the wood. Several of the trees are old poplars. The wood from these trees is known as poor firewood so I will donate it to a farmer who does much maple sugaring. He can use it quite satisfactorily when mixed with hardwood.

The farm is beautiful with lush, green grass. One can notice the growth of the grass is an inch or more overnight. The clover is thick, producing many four-leaf clovers. Flowers are maturing and blooming a month ahead of time.

Raspberries must be picked daily, rain or shine. The berries tend to drop off the branches and fall to the ground, laden with water. Some tend to mold. The berries make fine jelly and raspberry sauce, though they are not the most handsome to serve as fresh fruit. It takes a gentle hand not to shake the branches and lose half the crop to the ground where the berries are more difficult to pick up. Even dressed in a raincoat I come home drenched and cold.

The temperature hasn't risen into the nineties this year. Yesterday it hovered around 60 degrees Fahrenheit all day long and dropped to 55 degrees at night. This makes for pleasant cool evenings and a good night's sleep.

This summer has been hard on all farmers whose hopes are to harvest dry hay as well as the berry farmers who depend on the fruit for their livelihood. I have the luxury to be a bystander—an observer relishing variety and unpredictability.

Three New Arrivals

August 15, 1996

Some time ago Hooty the Owl was not on the shelf next to Harlequin Bear. "Where is Hooty the Owl?" I inquire of the bear.

"He left to see to the other circus companions. He flew out the chimney the evening when you failed to close the fireplace door and all the windows were closed because of rainstorms."

"Will he return? I'd miss him sorely if he left for good," I say with concern.

"He'll be back soon, I'm quite certain," Harlequin Bear says assuringly. "Leave the fireplace doors open so he can return when he pleases. He is just worried other circus animals may have escaped somewhere in Massachusetts and be lost. Hooty will find them and direct their travel to the farm. It is such a good place for us animals."

"Will the farm be the new home for all escaped animals? It might become quite crowded," I declare.

"Winter is approaching and we all need a roof over our head. Then, too, you like our presence and we are great at amusing you when you feel ill or sad. You and I both know this all too well."

"Indeed, there is no way to deny these facts. All of you animals have cooked up these ideas I suppose. The other day when I wanted to give one of you to a friend, I received a very sad look from each of you and then I did not have the heart to part with any of you."

"We are all grateful to be here. Hooty will be home soon. Furnace Brook Farm is home now."

The next morning, Hooty, who was now a soot-covered, tired looking owl, was back on the shelf with his companions.

"Where have you been and what have you been up to?" I inquire, with no response from the owl.

In the evening the news breaks. Louise and Dimp, Tom's mother, have a large, clear plastic traveling bag with a note for me. The bag contains three more escapees from the circus. Righty the Elephant, Lefty the Donkey (how did *he* ever land in a circus?) and Curly the Bear. They all have a heart-shaped red tag in their left ear with the letters TY (Tumbling Youngsters? or maybe Truly Yours?) printed on the tag. The initials are obviously those of the circus to which the animals belonged. The note from Tom suggests the animals need a home, for they were lost on the roads near Wellesley, U.S. Route 128, to be precise. The elephant was arguing with his friends to turn right—as his name Righty suggests he would—and the donkey said, "No! Left!" Lefty always knows the way. Fortunately Curly the Bear was there to mediate. He, being utterly independent and original, suggested getting out of the rain and taking shelter in a large, clear plastic bag. From there the animals could observe the world safely.

"Just wait a while and an independent sort of person will find us and take us in the direction of our destiny," Curly instructs. He continues reassuringly, "It is the way it always happens."

Then Hooty the Owl finds the lost animals sheltered in the "window bag," as he described the enclosure they were in. He decides to whisper the location of the lost animals into the ear of Tom. Now Tom comes into the act. He picks up the weary animals, carries them to his store and urges his mom to take them home to Vermont, a long way from the circus from which the animals had escaped.

The three companions, Righty, Lefty, and Curly received a nice blanket of tissue paper. They are well wrapped, so no spying circus attendant could find them in the window bag. They land on the back seat of the car belonging to Tom's mom. Weariness takes over. All discussion of going right or left ceases. Now that the animals were united under one large tent they allowed the independent rule of life, which Curly had introduced, to decide their fate.

Hooty the Owl located the three escapees as he explored the contents of the car. The owl peered through the window and heard some grumbling about "Right! No! Left!" Hooty knew at once these were his old friends from the circus who are forever arguing. Curly waved to the owl with his brown paw poking out of the window bag.

"All is well, Hooty. Just make sure we are taken to the farm where Harlequin Bear is located. We have been lost and lonely for some time, not to mention hungry."

"You needn't worry," Hooty says reassuringly. "In life both the unexpected and the least expected occurs when faith holds up. Righty and Lefty seem to have little faith in the ingenuity of people who do the correct, or expedient thing in spite of themselves. The wisdom of the owl would help them greatly. Unfortunately this wisdom is reserved for owls like me. I'll do my best. Go to sleep and get some rest, Curly."

With this having been said, the owl flies off into the evening, heading home to Chittenden at Furnace Brook Farm. The farm is easy to locate in moonlight. It is close to a waterfall where the water sparkles like a beacon late at night. Hooty has wonderful directional sense. He circles the river and the waterfall, picks up a field mouse for his supper, and then descends the chimney at the farm. Getting covered with soot is not much to his liking. He knows the car in which Righty, Lefty, and Curly are traveling has a Vermont license plate and he knows Tom can trust his mom to reunite old friends.

The next day I drive to Rutland to visit my friend Louise. She has in her arm the window bag which contains the three circus animals, Righty the Elephant, Lefty the Donkey, and Curly the Bear. Dimp had delivered the animals to Louise's home at Tom's request, expecting that I might be there, or else would soon show up.

Upon arrival at the farm there is quite a reunion! Harlequin Bear greets Curly Bear with a huge, warm hug. "Long time, no see. Are you all right? Have you come to stay? Will you miss the circus? You've had quite an adventure. Were you able to prevail on Righty and Lefty? Did they ever stop arguing? You are quite a mediator. It makes sense to be independent and have faith in life. Curly Bear, you are a wonderful example of the way we all should think and act. Will you become one of our leaders? I think you will. Masked Bear will want to make your acquaintance, as well as OUR BEAR and Paddington Bear. Where do you want to locate? The upper shelf is occupied by some strange animals such as the raccoon, the convertible caterpillar, and the honorable, old Heidelberg Lion. On the bottom shelf there are only our kind—all the bears in one row. I'm inclined to urge Righty and Lefty to stay on the upper shelf with the others and Hooty the Owl. The latter may be able to impart some wisdom to these unlikely friends and companions. Don't mention the words integration or segregation. It is family—the family of bears, don't you know."

"So, I will be the leader of the second shelf animals? It will do for now," Curly Bear agrees. "When Righty the elephant and Lefty the donkey become too unruly, I'll have to intervene for the sake of peace. I can always stand on your shoulders, Harlequin Bear, and hoist myself to the upper shelf in case of need. I'm glad to leave the argumentative ones to themselves for a while."

Righty and Lefty settle for the top shelf without so much as a sound for now. They are exhausted from their escapade and the long trip to Vermont. In any event, they are inherently pleased to be on the top shelf in my living room. Righty the Elephant and Lefty the Donkey voice no objections and seem in agreement for once.

And so the wanderers have come to a safe haven thanks to Tom, Dimp, Louise, and myself. All's well that ends well!

The animals wish to express their gratitude to all their friends. In case you do not already know, friends, time, and health cannot be bought with money, so why spend time performing in the circus?

Meet Righty and Lefty

August 16, 1996

The year 1996 is an exceptionally political year in the United States. In this year the president for the nation will be elected—or re-elected—by a vote of its citizens. This has been going on for some time. The vote is renewed every four years.

Many years ago the elephant was chosen mascot for the Republican party. This political party is convinced it is always right. When the elephant was born in the circus, the manager named him Righty. This name made the elephant special among all circus beasts.

The donkey grazing in a pasture nearby joined the circus to give voice to the fact that he too is of importance in the politics of this great country. "The letter D stands for donkey but also for Democrat," he neighed at the circus manager, who was not amused. The manager informed the donkey that Democrats are liberals and lean to the left. The donkey stubbornly followed the circus manager announcing over and over again, "Donkey stands for Democrat!"

When the donkey refused to turn home and the manager became tired of the donkey's tirade he turned to the animal and said, "All right, join the circus, but first I will have to paint an American flag on your rump or else nobody will pay any attention to you. You are not the usual circus animal." The donkey was overjoyed. He had won over the manager and was going to join "important" animals.

Righty the Elephant insisted the donkey be called Lefty so there would be no confusion between the two political parties they represented. They both had gray skin, unpretentious tails, and rather long ears. The animals at least needed clearly different names relating to their party. So, it was decided: R was for Republican and Righty; D was for Democrat and Donkey. Democrats are liberal and lean to the left, therefore Lefty. Not as simple as it may seem.

Righty and Lefty lead the opening parade of animals in the circus, followed by Curly the Bear, who is a staunch independent, waving a flag but without a paint jog on his rump. Then come the lions, followed by monkeys riding a string of zebras. They are always politically loyal to one or the other party. Then walk in clowns with parrots on their shoulders, never missing a political joke, always gabbing to the press and politically unreliable. Last are the acrobats and high-wire artists. These are the least political, unlikely to cast a vote, more interested in their art than power and politics.

After months of being the lead animal, the elephant is indignant at having to share the limelight with the donkey. They begin to argue at each turn in the road and every conceivable aspect of life. "I'm right, I'm right—you are a donkey to my left,

Lefty." The elephant could reason, argue, and object only in vain as Lefty, with his stubborn donkey nature, never yielded a pace. Occasionally when the commotion reached such a pitch the performance of the circus nearly came to a halt. Then Curly the independent bear would gently, but firmly, intervene. "We live on a round planet called Earth. If you, Righty, keep going to the right long enough and you, Lefty, go to the left, you both will cross over at the other side of the world and then Righty will stand to the left of Lefty. You'd better go straight ahead and remember you all live under the same tent with all the other animals and people. Enough is enough. I'll be glad when the election is over on November 4th, then things will fall back into a more normal political life. Peace and quiet may set in again. Reasoning, what I am best at, may come to the forefront. It is the best way to deal with complex problems, though I do not expect a circus of diverse animals to ever quite grasp this concept."

An Unexpected Visitor

August 17, 1996

The other day I opened the overhead door into the garage. I had a bag of trash in my arms for disposal. I see a chipmunk scurry so fast out of the garage I stop to say half out loud to myself, "You're in a hurry. What is this rush all about?" I'm fully aware the chipmunk has other means of egress—namely the small, back door into the garage which I keep open all summer for air circulation. There are no windows in the garage so humidity and stagnant air accumulate quickly. So why this wild dash?

Soon the cause becomes self-evident. A red-shouldered hawk is parked in the middle of the garage floor. The bird spreads its wings. In a few moments, swish-swish, it flies toward the opening of the overhead door, and takes off into freedom. This hawk has a wingspan of three feet or so. The coloring is that of an immature red-shouldered hawk: brownish, mottled upper parts and a cream or buff underside with dark streaks or blotches. It too was pleased to escape from the garage. I speculate the bird followed the chipmunk into the garage by the small door but became trapped by its large wingspan unable to fly out the small entrance. The hawk no longer showed any interest in the chipmunk. It's flight was up into the sky and off towards it's large nest near the brook. Well, that was indeed an unexpected visitor.

This hawk is in residence near the brook, which explains why the bird feeders have remained full for a week or two. The squirrels and blue jays have been out of sight. No squawking from the jays was most noticeable. I thought in mid-summer my friends had tired of their steady diet of sunflower seed and were savoring berries and other delicacies. Not so. They were a meal for the hawk or they have taken flight into the woods and another territory. Now the hawk polices the farmyard, circulating high overhead. For the wee animals, he is a dangerous specter in the sky. Only occasionally the chipmunk and one solitary chickadee come to the feeder. Beware of the one hawk! I suppose they are aware of the danger lurking in the sky.

This winter will the jays and squirrels return?

The Window Visitor

August 25, 1996

There is a thump again at my window in the den, which soon turns into a rather persistent knocking. Oh, I know, surely it is Green Mountain Bear. He hasn't been around for several weeks. I wonder what he has been up to? I open the window and hear an excited grunt. I call to him, "Welcome, little friend and visitor, where have you been?"

"Where have you been is the question! The window has been closed and you have been in no mood to welcome me," the bear announces somewhat indignantly.

"Come, come, what a wrong idea. It is getting cool at night, and some of the rainstorms have been fierce. So, I keep the window closed as I have in early spring and late fall last year. By now you should know you are most always welcome. With fall approaching fast, you will have to make your presence known by tapping on the window, but don't use a stick because window glass is breakable. You are getting bigger and stronger each time you come around."

"As you say, winter is on its way. I know, I've been eating plenty of berries and I have caught trout in the brook. The trout are small but tasty. I came to say thank you for clearing the waterfall of large fallen poplars. They obstructed my swimming hole and the pool where I'm likely to catch a trout without too much effort. But as for fallen trees, you could have left the other three trees that fell across the brook further downstream just where they were. These made marvelous walkways for the animals. We did not have to get wet wading across the brook nor take a detour to the cement bridges. You were not thinking of me, were you?"

"Let me explain. If the large trees are left in the brook, ice dams form in winter, the water backs up, and may flood the road which makes travel more treacherous. You would not understand, for at that time of year you are sound asleep in your den, deep in hibernation."

"Hmmm . . . why don't *you* go into hibernation during that time of year?" the bear asks inquisitively.

"Sometimes I think that might be a good idea. Winter is long and cold in New England. Many people travel south to Florida, they are known as 'snow birds.' It is no longer in the makeup of man to hibernate, though if the weather is terrible— with sleet, snow and ice storms for several day— one sometime stays at home for a prolonged period, close to the warm fire in the stove or fireplace."

"If I had a snug, warm fire by which to cuddle up, would I hibernate? I doubt it. Maybe I should stay indoors at the farm this winter, with all the stuffed animals. I'd thrive on milk and honey, and I'd be better company than my stuffed equivalents."

"What do you mean, 'stuffed equivalents'? You just coined a new term for man-made friends. Stuffed equivalents is not very flattering. Are you jealous of OUR BEAR, Paddington Bear, Masked Bear, Harlequin Bear, and Curly Bear? They fill a need and permit me to grant you your freedom. If I had no stuffed equivalents, as you call my menagerie of bears, you'd be in danger of being domesticated. In the long run you would not like it. As a matter of fact I'm quite certain I may not wish to run after a bear all day long, tending to his needs. Then, too, you are very talkative."

"I'm only talkative because I'm on my own for long periods of time. No different than you yourself. That is why you write. It makes up for lack of verbal communication. Writing is your talk equivalent. For all I know the piano sounds you make serve the same purpose."

"You are being very smart this evening," I remark. Who taught you the term 'equivalent'?"

"I'm sure I picked it up from you sometime earlier in our conversations. What does it really mean?"

"According to the dictionary it is a term denoting to have equal power; equal in force, amount or value."

"Then you will have to admit the stuffed animals are important to you, are they not? Are they equal to me? That is unlikely."

"They are a substitute only," I reply, "and good for times when you don't come around."

"I hear you all too well, but how can I be free to do my own thing in life and be here at the same time?"

"You can't. That is why I have the stuffed equivalents so I do not impose on you and deprive you of your freedom unintentionally."

"That is really very nice," he admits. "I did not see it that way at first."

"It helps to talk things over. Last, but not least, don't spend a moment being jealous. It is a complete waste of time; a means of gradually, and progressively destroying your soul and happiness."

"Is that the lesson or moral of the day? I'll have to take it under advisement and talk it over with Mountain Lion and some of my other friends. Trouble is they only like to gossip when they bother to stop and talk at all."

"To change the topic . . . please thank the moose for sparing the raspberry bushes by the house and spending the summer in the national forest. Then, too, it is nice you didn't overturn Jim's beehives. By the way, though the apple harvest is meager this fall, the tree by the waterfall is dropping some apples. These are for you as well as loads of crabapples on the tree by the entrance to the farm. I'll use some for jelly and you may come and help yourself to the rest."

"Thanks, I'll be on my way now. 'Good evening,' as you like to say."

"Yes, good evening to you also. Take care."

There is a thud in the grass and off goes the bear. I'm quite fond of this strange friend of mine. I can hear him say, "I'm only a thought equivalent," chuckling as he goes his way.

Reflections

Labor Day, 1996

We have had a beautiful summer with maybe just a little too much rain. The daisies blossomed generously on the farm and enhanced the meadows. Red, pink, and white clover thrived with the abundance of rain. There were plenty of four-leaf clovers for friends and visitors. The flowers by the homestead responded to care and plant food. The roses, each one more beautiful than the next, allowed some elegant photos to be taken. These will make nice cards to mail to friends during the long winter months which we will be facing soon.

Then the landscape will be white, gray, and many shades of brown and black. There will be no soft pinks, reds, or yellows to brighten the picture. The exuberance of color during spring and summer makes these months such a visual treasure. Fall will bring bright foliage for a brief period—the farewell of the warm months.

The glorious blue sky will be a rarity in November and during the winter months. The days will be pewter gray, sometimes for weeks on end. A subdued elegance with delicate shades of gray, and other muted tones.

It takes a different frame of mind to enjoy winter days. It requires more self reliance and inner resources to survive when nature turns inward. It is a time of dormancy, which allows imagination and creativity to take hold with story writing and

Daisies in abundance.

music making. Books become important—ideas are more freely exchanged with friends than in summer, when one is busy outdoors.

Long walks along the brook in deep snow have their very own charm. Animal tracks and birds at the feeder are suddenly important again.

The summer breeze is replaced by fierce, howling wind and the Alberta clipper which indicates the arrival of snow and subzero temperature from Canada.

Lawnmowers are put in storage and snow-blowers are put to use.

We celebrate Christmas, the arrival of New Year, St. Valentine's Day, and Groundhog Day, and even Easter in some years before the snow melts and the fragrance of maple sap cooking in large vats permeates the countryside.

At times the year seems to rush by, but in cold, inclement weather time seems to slow down a bit—too much maybe.

Spring fever arrives invariably with a case of the flu thrown in for good luck. But then the days of muddy roads and melting snow, and the first snowdrop flowers bring the excitement of early springtime and the anticipation of color and mild days ahead.

Out at the farm the details of each change in weather is more noticeable and palpable than in towns and cities. In a rural environment life is richer in simpler ways than among the noise, clutter, and bustle of cars and people of urban centers. The farm is closer to the cycle of life as known to man for centuries. To some, life at the farm seems intimidating in its frugal elegance and lack of pretense. To each his own . . .

The Red Admiral

September 5, 1996

This butterfly is labeled as "unmistakable and unforgettable" by the *Audubon Society Field Guide to North American Butterflies*. At Furnace Brook Farm the sighting of this butterfly is an event. The Red Admiral may be a rare butterfly for our region because when showing the photograph to many friends, they each told me this is a new species of butterfly to them.

The Red Admiral . . . a rare visitor to the farm.

A Special Day

Three years ago, on September 9th, I took possession of the deed to Furnace Brook Farm. As I look back I have a good feeling. These years have been exhilarating with many new discoveries and much new learning. I have found the contentment I had as a young child on the farm in Austria—war, and solitary confinement notwithstanding. Then, as now, the farm is different every day. One is more aware of the weather here than in a city. Each day brings a new observation such as a new animal, a new flower, a new and different stone, or changes in the water level and color of the brook.

People are not as important as when living in a crowded community. There are no close neighbors, whose behavior has to be tolerated even if loud and offensive.

In the country there are berries, apples, and other crops. One barters for crops less abundant on one's farm for those which are a surplus at a neighbor's. It is a natural, easy exchange.

There is plenty of time to take a walk and consider the changes of the season and light in the heaven.

There is always some activity to keep one busy. The garden or woods are always in need of some attention if one desires to be engaged outdoors. Much is beyond my strength. Now, as then, the

Furnace Brook in autumn.

thrill at accomplishment remains the same. The contentment at the end of a day is special, and physical fatigue is a welcome experience after years of spending most of the day in an office or hospital. There is a closure I had not really expected.

Friends are treasured. At the farm they can arrive, stay a while, or a little longer, if they are so disposed. Friends know that sulking, bad temper, manipulative behavior, and intrigue do not agree

Brightly colored leaves in the brook.

with me. They have the intuition to refrain from this type of activity. Laughter and smiles are in natural abundance—it is like a breath of fresh air after years of dealing with sick people and keeping their needs in the forefront of one's mind. The practice of medicine has brought wonderful rewards, though very different than the life on a farm.

The Barn: Center of Attention!

September 11, 1996

Finally the barn will be painted and repairs will be made where necessary. This fall Jim Moore has time to devote to this project. First the structure is washed off with the use of a power hose. Bleach, water, and an antifungal agent removes the dust and black mold that has proliferated for some time. The barn has the appearance of being newly painted as the old red stain stands out.

Then Jim explores the condition of the two lean-tos. The sill has rotted away and the walls have pushed off their foundation on the building to the west. The structure was held up by a pile of old sawdust, or "hanging by a toothpick," as Jim describes the condition. A new sill is installed, two windows for ventilation are cut into the west wall and the south wall is converted to a large opening, elegantly dressed up with a triangle in the corner. The door frame is painted white. From a distance it is a handsome improvement to the looks of the barn. Now, air circulates and we have a convenient drive-thru. This change gives the lean-to the appearance of being part of the original structure, rather than that of an afterthought! Seen from the road, the new look mandates that the same improvement be made to the northeast lean-to. This will be less costly as it will require much less time and material. There is a general consensus among all of us that this

Jim painting the barn.

alteration will give the barn a handsome and stable appearance.

Jim paints while the sun is shining and leaves the carpentry work for later. The new paint is a real barn red. It applies with ease and uniformity. If it is resistant to mold for eleven years, as claimed by the manufacturer, this will be all to the good. The windows, door frames, and some trim will remain white, as in the past.

Gravel added to the front of entrances will make maintenance easier.

The refurbished barn after the first snowfall.

Time permitting, Jim will refurbish the inside of the barn so I can use the space to display some watercolors if I get busy enough and have an abundance of such. This improvement may be done in the fall or maybe it will wait until next spring.

For once I have taken before-and-after photographs to document the changes and to give to Jim as a memory of all the many hours of hard work he has devoted to this project.

A few days ago Katherine and Sally scrubbed the plastic overhead door at the main entrance to the lower part of the barn. Katherine exclaims that the door has never been washed. Now the door sparkles and enhances the good looks.

Some windows have lost their crossbars. Jim hopes to find some old windows to replace these and unify the appearance of the facade that can be seen from the road.

So far, all of us are enjoying the progress made each day.

Usually I keep a list on hand of things that need doing. To everyone's amusement Katherine added to Jim's list, "Please paint the barn, but not the cow!"

Color Surrounds the Pond

September 14, 1996

This year the pond by the house looks spectacular. A mass of yellow blossoms, thick and dense, are growing in the water at the rim of the pond. Neither Katherine, Sally, nor I recall its presence in prior years. The flowers may be in full bloom and glorious because the water level in the pond is lower than usual, allowing the seeds to burst open and the flowers to mature. Several friends

The pond edged with yellow blossoms.

61

have asked for the name of this charming flower. The plant is called the Nodding Burr Marigold or Sticktight. Numerous flower heads per plant have six to ten bright yellow petals around the yellow-brown disk center. The fruit consists of four slender barbed bristles, or awns. The barbed fruit account for the name Sticktight.

Higher on the bank of the pond are bright purple New England asters as well as purple-stemmed asters with pink-to-white petal-like rays. Goldenrod abounds in the midst of the asters. The thicket of wildflowers is a visual treat!

Change of Season

September 24, 1996

September 17, 18, and 19 were three pristine days. Everyone without exception commented about the weather. No wonder . . . sunshine, a few clouds, gentle breezes, and the mild temperature was deceptive for this time of year. It allowed outdoor work to progress nicely. Jim worked diligently on the barn, painting and making repairs as he went along.

Then torrential rain and thunderstorms bring gray days, cool weather, and the arrival of fall. Last night we experienced the first frost at the farm, although mild enough to spare some flowers in protected enclaves. Wool jackets are suddenly in vogue again.

This morning a phone call alerts us that Jim's Mom has taken ill. Soon Jim is on his way to the hospital. A pall falls upon all of us at the farm. By noon Jim phones to advise me that his mother will be hospitalized for several days. He is busy supporting the family and tending to sundry duties. Wishes of a prompt recovery for his mother are all we can offer.

Finally, at the bird feeders, one blue jay, one goldfinch, one titmouse, and one chickadee return to feast on sunflower seeds. No squirrels are in sight. The red-shouldered hawk has stopped circling the farm for a few days. Perhaps the bird has moved on.

Looking back over the summer, the absence of hummingbird moths is evident, suggesting that the summer might not have been warm enough. Each year is so different from the next, why do I expect the return of the same visitors each season? Maybe there is some unexplained comfort in continuity.

Today I managed to get the lawn tractor stuck in the mud once again. Katherine laughed good-naturedly. "You were looking for another story, that's all!" she announces as she comes to my

Change of seasons.

rescue. With the help of the six-foot chain and my car, we pull the tractor out of the ditch. Don't ask what the lawn looks like! Two deep brown ruts are evidence of the mishap, which Sally and Katherine try to conceal by filling the holes with dirt. In time grass will grow in. In the meantime I chalk my experience up as food for thought. I drove too close to the ditch—and gently slid into the mud—with the best of intentions of reducing the work for the small lawnmowers. Intentions are one thing, the outcome is another. Maybe I will learn one of these days . . . and, then again, maybe I won't! It has been quite a while, so maybe I was due to get stuck in the mud. The year is nearly over and this was one of the last chances to bog down. Now, how could I miss the opportunity? I'm delighted I didn't need more than my car and a chain to undo the mess. The tractor continued to purr the rest of the afternoon. However, I turned the machine over to Sally. Once stuck in the mud is enough for one day. Sally is a more cautious driver than I am.

Time to Take Shelter

September 28, 1996

It has been a gorgeous fall day at the farm. The leaves are turning yellow rapidly. The grass continues to grow lush and green.

While reading *The Slab City Messenger* to catch up on local news, I find on the back page a notice, "Bear Hunting Season Until November 20th. Hunters took 380 bears in the 1995 season, the fourth year in a row that the total has been more than 300." It continues, "Fall bear food was scarce so bears traveled extensively and denned up early for the winter."

I immediately think about Green Mountain Bear and hope that he stops by so I can caution him to take shelter until Thanksgiving. As I am mulling over my thoughts, there is a gentle knock at the den window and the trace of dirty paw marks on the newly washed window informs me it is indeed my little friend.

I open the window and greet the bear, "Welcome, I'm so glad you came calling this evening. Where have you been? It seems like a long time since your last visit."

"Did you miss me?" he asks.

"Of course, at least a little. After all, friends are precious, and when one loses contact for too long, concern takes over."

"How long is too long?" he wonders.

"I can't tell you, this is an individual judgment,"

I reply. There is a long pause in our conversation as the bear considers my answer.

"I've been very busy," comes the reply (or possibly the excuse).

"What have you been up to?" I question, suspecting the little bear is bursting with news he is anxious to share with me.

"I've been gathering and eating all the beechnuts and acorns I can find in the woods. There are many beech trees to the west of your barn and several large oak trees. One of the largest oak trees I've seen in this region was once struck by lightning, yet it survived and grew to stand above all other trees. The acorns are bountiful, though the squirrels try to get the majority. They hide the acorns in the soil. I don't hide the acorns, I eat them. They are so delicious!"

"The oak tree you refer to is large indeed. Katherine measured the circumference of the tree a year ago. It came to 11 feet-3 inches at chest height. I'm glad the tree has many acorns. Aren't you grateful to the squirrels for cutting the branches bearing the nuts, so you do not have to climb a tree which is too big for you?"

"Oh, yes, I'm appreciative. At this time of year I'm especially hungry, so I have little inclination to share the acorns with other animals. The squirrels can't be very hungry if all they do is hide the acorns. I think their intention is to tease me, as far as I know."

"That is not quite the way it is," I explain. "You hibernate through the long winter. Squirrels need to eat all year long. They even dig through a foot of snow to retrieve buried nuts. The squirrel may not remember where it buried the nuts but he can smell them under a foot of snow. When snow is deep, the animal tunnels under the snow to get closer to the scent."

"Then I really should not uncover their trove of hidden nuts and raid their winter supply?"

"You'll have to decide that for yourself."

"I'll have to think about this," the bear ponders. "What else have you been doing?"

"I'm den cleaning," the bear boasts.

"What is that all about?" I ask a trifle incredulous.

"Oh, you should see me. The dust flies. All the old bedding—the leaves from last fall—are scraped out of my den. Then I put down the plastic garbage bag you gave me and fill the den with fresh, dry leaves. The den smells sweet and wonderful. It was worth all the effort. In one back corner I have the winter sweater from last year which I will only wear in the den before I go into deep hibernation. I'm all set for winter now. I can go and feed at my leisure and watch you from a distance as you work about the farm, wearing the bright orange vest. I still think the vests are elegant, though I suspect it is not the garb for a Green Mountain Bear."

68

"Well, I'm glad you are doing well and are contented. There is sad news I have to give you, though. The local newspaper announces that bear hunting season is on until November 20. You, little friend, could be in danger."

"I thought man only hunted deer and turkeys. Since when do they hunt bear?"

"I suppose for centuries. Man likes to have your beautiful fur for a blanket in winter, and some even eat your meat. I'm sorry, little bear, to have to give you this bad news."

"You don't hunt bears, do you?" the bear inquires in a frightened voice.

"No, I'm not a hunter."

"May I ask you what I can do to protect myself?"

"Stay in your den until it gets dark," I warn, "and then remain close by, in territory you know well. If you get lonesome or depressed, come and call on me in the evening when you see light in the house. I've posted the land so hunters are not to shoot within 500 feet of any building. Would they abide by the law if they saw you and were after a black bear? I hope so, but I cannot be sure."

"This is terrible news. I don't like it a bit. Is there anything you can do to change the law so bears are not taken in fall? Do these end up in a circus like Masked Bear did? Is this what happened to my mother and brother last fall?"

"'Taken' in this news article means killed. It is a euphemism, the substitution of an agreeable or inoffensive expression for one that may offend or suggest something unpleasant," I explain.

"Then man has declared war on us. We have no good way to fight back. Our only defense is to den up for the duration of this dreadful time of year. I'm glad I have you as a friend and you shared the bad news with me. Thanksgiving will be special for bears. The hunt will be over and I will be free to roam the woods once more. Then I will come calling again."

"Take care, now. Ask the blue jays to alert your beloved in the national forest. Don't make the trip yourself, this could be too dangerous."

"Well taken."

I see tears in the eyes of the bear as he quietly moves on. I too shed a tear or two. I'd hate to lose my friend. By now I hope he trusts me and will heed my advice.

What Will This Winter Be Like?

October 4, 1996

This morning we have the first serious frost of the season. The temperature plummeted to minus 20 degrees Fahrenheit. The fields are white with frost, the flowers are hanging their heads and the wind is blowing leaves off the trees. It feels bitter cold, though this is just the beginning of things to come! In fact, this is a late frost—usually we get the killing frost around mid-September. This year we had our last fresh corn as late as the first of October, another exception to the rule.

In four days the last major job at the farm will take place: the planting of daffodil and tulip bulbs to dress up next spring. The weather may be cold but rain may hold off until later in the week.

The barn has been painted and some weak walls have been strengthened. Jim is finishing off the windows which are in need of putty and white paint.

Snow probably has already fallen in higher elevations. This makes for special beauty. The bright fall colors in the valley complemented by white-capped mountaintops is a glorious sight.

This time of year gives the opportunity to devote more time to the piano, settle in to enjoy the wood fire in the fireplaces, and let things come the way it may.

When I inquire of a native, "What will this winter be like?" the answer comes with a big smile, "I'll tell you next spring!" This is the voice of experience.

This weather makes me turn to the L.L. Bean catalogue from which I can order necessary warm clothes. I've been putting off this job for some time. No rush, I keep saying to myself. This morning I am wiser!

In late November I'll have occasion to do wildlife photography at Mountain Top Inn. The animals will arrive from Montana—bears, mountain lions, and a variety of small animals. I'll have the opportunity to try a Hasselblad and a Canon camera, for the companies making these cameras are sponsoring the four-day event right in my back yard!

A Terrified Green Mountain Bear

October 26, 1996

Loud pounding against the den window startles me late at night while I am asleep in my bedroom. The windows are open as is my custom, thus I cannot possibly miss this commotion downstairs. It must be Green Mountain Bear, but what brings him around past midnight and in obvious distress? The pounding continues until I reach the den window. Cautiously I open the window so as not to scare the bear even more, and to make sure it is he and not some other animal or human.

"What has happened to you?" I inquire.

"I'm as scared as never before in my life. I need to talk to you. Will you please listen closely to my story and help me if you can?"

"Why, of course," I reassure, "that's what a friend is for. Are you injured or hurt, like Mountain Lion was last fall?"

"No, but nearly. I'm terrified by the events of the day."

"You had a close call?"

"Was it ever! And this is only the beginning."

"Calm down. Get your thoughts together, and tell me why you are so terrified."

There is a pause of some duration while the bear takes a few deep breaths, sighs, and shakes his head. The light from the room outlines his shape against the dark of the night.

"I nearly lost my life, and that is not all. More trouble is on its way."

"Now, do calm down," I repeat, "and tell me exactly what occurred. Let me hold your paw, it might comfort you." Without hesitation the bear extends a mud-covered, cold, wet paw. After a minute or so I inquire, "There, are you feeling a little better now?"

"Well, yes," he says a bit more composed. He hesitates a while, then the bear begins his story.

"It all started out fine in the morning. I ventured from my den and climbed up my favorite beech tree which is located close to my den. Last summer I built a large comfortable nest with branches in this tree. It is a cool, pleasant place to spend a hot night and from here it is easy to reach beechnuts. I was enjoying a good meal of them when I hear the jays screeching. They fly overhead and tell me a hunter and his large black dog are approaching from the north. I dare not remain in the tree, so I scamper down and dash into my den. I thought I'd be safe . . . you know, 'out of sight, out of mind.' The jays continue to divebomb over the den and keep me informed the hunter is coming closer and closer. The black dog is sniffing near my den. I hear the hunter tell his dog, 'Find that black bear.' I'm so scared I can hardly move. I hear the dog real close by. The opening to my den is large enough to enable the dog to easily get into my den. I am concerned whether I will be able to fend off the dog and the hunter. Quickly I tear a rock out of the side of my den and shove it with all my strength against the den opening which was none too soon. Amidst loud baying and barking I see the paw of the dog enter the den entrance where the rock did not cover completely. I put all my weight and strength against the rock so the dog can't dislodge it. I dare not bite his paw, for then the dog would know I'm in the den and then I'd be a goner."

Green Mountain Bear continues, "Then the dog starts to dig around my entrance. I stay frozen, holding the rock firmly in place. Time is endless. I get exhausted from exerting so much effort, but you must understand I am fearing for my life. This has never happened to me in the past. Finally the dog tires and the hunter calls the dog off the dig. 'You stupid dog, that black bear isn't there,' I hear the hunter yell. I expect the dog and hunter will move on. No such luck. They settle right in front of my den and rest in the sunlight. The hunter talks out loud. 'I saw a black bear in a beech tree but the critter got away. I don't understand how. I'll hang around the rest of the day. The bear may show up again. His den must be close by. See you this evening.' Here the bear pauses, then questions, "To whom was the man talking?"

I explain, "He probably had a cellular phone and talked to a friend at camp or his family. To you it may have only looked like a small portable box with numbers on it."

"Whatever . . . from my den I saw nothing."

"It must have been strenuous guarding the entrance to your den with that rock."

"Oh, very!" he exclaims.

"What happened next?"

"I heard this chewing noise. Later, when it was pitch dark, they left. I found the cores of several apples left behind at the front of my entrance. This was small consolation."

"So . . . you got away all right," I say to the bear consolingly .

"My story is not yet over! It gets more frightening, and here is where I need your help."

"Then, go on," I encourage.

"The hunter must have fallen asleep after he had finished eating. I heard distinct loud snoring. Then he talked out loud, probably not to his dog but to someone on the other end of the thing you call a cellular phone."

"What did he say?" I inquire, wondering if this story will ever come to an end. Green Mountain Bear is taking much time to tell his woes.

"The hunter said, 'Tell Johnny to go out in the barn and find the bear traps which belonged to Grandfather Joe. Tomorrow I'll set the traps and I'll get me a bear alright!" and the man chuckled gleefully. I know this is serious trouble. I do not know what a bear trap is, so please help me before it is too late." The bear yanks his paw from my hand so as to conceal his trembling.

"Green Mountain Bear, I'm so glad you came for advice and help. Bear traps are a serious problem, especially if you don't know what they look like and what they can do to an animal. Bear traps are made of heavy iron metal. They have a loaded spring and when you or any other animal goes for the food—the so-called bait—and you touch the trap, the spring will release and trap your paw in such a way that you will have great pain and be unable to free your paw. Sometimes, in desperation, an animal will tear so hard at the trap as to sever the limb. From then on life is difficult and sad. Perhaps your neck may be caught in the spring which could cost you your life. Traps are dreadful inventions. They are a means of capturing animals when they are unsuspecting and often hungry. These traps have been outlawed, I believe, but then if a mean person uses those from the past it can be hard to find the culprit and punish the person breaking the law."

"What to do about this serious problem?"

I assess the situation, "First of all, traps are often covered with sticks and leaves so as to disguise their presence. Anything that looks disturbed or different, don't go near—especially if you can smell meat or other food morsels. Never be curious about a trap—stay away! Watch where you are walking. Take your time and learn to be very very cautious. Ask the jays to watch for hunters and observe if they are carrying anything other than their guns and regular backpack. The jays should observe where the traps are placed and report this to you immediately.

When you inform me, I'll make sure that Katherine, Sally, and I go looking for the traps. We will spring them, deactivate the devices, and then remove them if we are able to hoist them. Then, too, I will alert the game warden to do all he can to catch the perpetrator and punish the rascal. Even humans have to be careful not to get badly injured by a bear trap."

"Can I put a stick into the trap and deactivate it that way?"

"I think traps are far too dangerous for you to fool around with. One more thing, you need to warn all other animals about the traps, especially your friend Mountain Lion and her two cubs. Although, the fox and coyote are in just as much danger. All animals should be alerted until such time as the woods are safe again. Be sure to thank the jays for all their help. This surely is a vexing problem."

"A what?" the bear asks.

"A vexing problem . . . or should we call it troubling and distressing?"

"The better term is 'terrifying'. I've lived through it. I know!"

"Come again whenever it seems safe. Remember, you have a friend at Furnace Brook Farm."

"I know, and thanks," the bear says gratefully.

"Had the last word again?"

"Always!" the bear replies smartly and then is off into the darkness.

I stay awake a long time pondering the nature of man.

The Follow-up

October 28, 1996

Knock-knock, or is it more a scratch-scratch on the lowest windowpane in the den. Oh, I know, it will be Green Mountain Bear with news from the woodland.

"Hi," I said.

"Hi to you."

"Feeling better this evening?" I inquire.

"Yes, much."

"So what is the news? Did the hunter return with his dog and bear trap?"

"I stayed in my den all day listening for the dog and the voice of his master. I heard nothing. The jays patrolled the area with regular fly-overs. They saw no hunters in the woods today."

"What a relief!"

"Did you talk to the game warden?" the bear asks expectantly.

"Not yet," I reply.

"What do you think happened?"

"Green Mountain Bear, there are many explanations I can come up with, and all may be incorrect."

"Well, what do you suspect happened?"

"Maybe Johnny couldn't find the bear trap in the old barn."

"That would be splendid!"

"Or maybe the trap is so rusty it will need to be polished and cleaned before putting it to use, which is only a matter of time."

"Not so splendid," the bear says with disappointment.

"Maybe the hunter had to return to work on Monday and may only have time to hunt on weekends."

"You think there is a chance he'll show up in a few days?"

"Yes, a small chance."

"That is a dreadful possibility," says the bear despairingly. "It means I'll have to listen and be on the watch-out from now on."

"You'd better remain open to this alternative," I warn.

"Ugh!"

"Ugh, indeed!"

"That I didn't want to hear."

"You have the help of the jays. They are likely to warn you, aren't they?"

"Sure, but it is not the same as being care-free and fancy-free."

"You want to stay alive and well. Caution will be important until the hunting season has passed, which will be about a week or so after Thanksgiving time."

"Will you give me a dish of honey and warm milk for my Thanksgiving?"

"Sure I will."

"It will at least be a small consolation for all this caution and vigilance I have to display until it is time to hibernate. By the way, I assured the jays you will keep the birdfeeders well supplied with sunflower seed this winter as a thank-you for their service in patrolling the woods for me."

"Did you? Not a bad deal, I'd say. You are quite smart when it comes for others to pay back your debt of gratitude."

"I have little else to offer them."

"It's quite all right. I'll feed the jays in any event."

"Thanks, I thought you would. Also, I give my apologies for waking you up the other night. The misery of the day and my fear had gotten out of control."

"That is understandable. I'm glad you felt free to call."

"My imagination got the better of me and it was very terrifying."

"Don't dwell on the past. Hopefully you will get only a bad scare and receive no injury before winter comes."

"I'll see to it," he assures.

"There you go. Keep a positive attitude."

"Have you spoken to Mountain Lion and warned some of the other animals?"

"I've sent word by the jays. Mountain Lion will drop by in a day or so. The cubs and lioness are in the national forest. They travel mostly by night, so it could be tomorrow before they arrive at my den. I'm looking forward to their visit. It has been lonesome all by myself in the den. It is too early to hibernate and venturing out has been no fun at all. There were many shots in the valley three days ago."

"Yes, I know. Katherine, Sally, and I heard the guns go off. I asked one of the hunters on his way home if he had shot or seen a bear. He told me he hadn't."

"So you knew I was all right?"

"I thought it was likely."

"So you check up on matters of the woodland in your own way."

"I can't forget about my special friend, or, should I?"

"Well it seems we are here for each other and to help protect the other animals."

"I think so."

"Well, then, time to be on my way."

"Take care."

"I'll try to. Say hi to Katherine and Sally for me. Someday maybe I'll meet them."

"Maybe," I agree.

"So long now." There is a soft thud as the bear leaves the windowsill and is on his way. The full moon this evening will make the return through the woods to his den easier.

Green Mountain Bear Comes Calling

November 9, 1996

It is a mild evening. Snow which has been predicted for two days has not yet fallen. In my den I'm reading a book by Ernest Lawrence Rossi, *The Psychobiology of Mind-Body Healing.* It is a fascinating summary of advances made in my lifetime about the concept of stress and its effect on the autonomic nervous system, the endocrine system, and immune system. I pause to open the window for some fresh air. For once I have a fire crackling in the fireplace when none is needed for warmth. Apples baking in the oven are filling the air with a delicious aroma. Before I know it, I hear a sniffing sound and scratching by the open window. Then the all-familiar voice of Green Mountain Bear announces, "Hi! I'm here!"

"Yes, I heard you at the window. What brings you calling?"

"I needed to stretch, take a walk, and get some fresh air. I guess I got bored in my den all week long. Tell me, what smells so delicious? Standing at this window I get a wonderful whiff of something."

"I am baking apples in the oven."

"Baked apples? Don't you eat apples raw as I do?"

"Not always. I like to bake some with raisins, cloves, and maple syrup, especially when I expect company."

"So, you baked these apples for me? I'd love to taste one."

"You'd like to taste one?"

"Well, aren't I considered company?" he says, a bit insulted.

"First the apples will have to cool. Right now they are steaming hot."

"Maybe before I leave . . . I'm in no hurry this evening."

"You are acting rather human tonight."

"No, I doubt that . . . more animal I'd say. I don't shoot innocent animals nor do I set traps." The bear is nearly indignant at the very thought of being equated with humans.

"Any sign of hunters and traps on your side of the mountain?" I inquire.

"Not for the moment. I think it has been raining too heavily. Hunters don't like to get drenched, do they?"

"Probably not, though I wouldn't count on it. Tell me, did Mountain Lion and her cubs come calling?"

"Yes," the bear replies, "she stopped by with the cubs. Mountain Lion looks thin and tired—the cubs are a picture of health and they are playful. We talked a long time. Mountain Lion may move close to the brook for the winter. It is the fresh water and the many small animals she needs to hunt for to survive which may bring her into the valley. She is troubled that there are far fewer small squirrels and chipmunks than usual. We believe the hawks are very canny and have taken much of the prey that Mountain Lion needs. The hawks even took the four red squirrels and the three gray ones which fed at your feeder all year long. Did you know that?"

"I've suspected it. The squirrels disappeared in less than a week's time. I only have one little chipmunk at the feeder these days, and soon he will do as you and go into hibernation."

"That seems like a smart thing to do."

"Mountain Lion told me she dens up for a few weeks to have her kittens but prefers to roam the land all other times of the year."

"Yes, I've seen her tracks in the depth of winter."

"Now, tell me, have the baked apples cooled off enough? I can't wait much longer."

"I thought you said you weren't in much of a hurry this evening," I retort.

"It's all relative."

"Now, wait, I'll check on the apples." When I return with a plastic-coated plate and one of the baked apples, I hear a grunt of contentment and exhilaration.

"Here is a tasty meal for a special friend," I say as I place the morsel on the windowsill.

Gulp . . . chew . . . and vigorous licking of the plate follows. Then the bear makes a final comment, "A nice change from all the cold, sour apples I've been eating this fall. Maple syrup reminds me of early springtime. I think I'll dream of spring tonight when I get back to my den. Thanks, and have a nice evening."

"It's nice you stopped by. Take care."

The bear licks his chops and pushes the plastic plate back and forth, anxious to lick up all the sweet sauce. Then I hear a plunk and off he goes. He has no last words tonight. He is preoccupied by the thought of spring. Not a bad way to end the day. "Farewell, little fellow, watch out and don't get harmed, if you can help it." As I close the window I think of how much I'll miss him when his time comes.

The Indoor Fire Escape

November 3, 1996

Today John Sivret is here to replace some electrical outlets with a more modern version. We are changing to three-prong outlets with a built-in ground. While he is working in the upstairs guest room, where the aluminum-chain fire escape ladder is stored, it occurs to me it is time to make sure I am still nimble and strong enough to use the ladder in case of an emergency.

As a child of seven I was in a house fire on the family farm. This exceedingly frightening event has left me in need to check fire exits wherever I am. So, in 1993, within a week of purchasing the Furnace Brook Farm, while Jim Moore is working in the upstairs room redoing the floor, I untangle the chain-link ladder, hook it to the windowsill, and courageously descend onto the lawn outdoors. I think it takes more time than I'd have in a raging fire. Nevertheless, I am reassured and store the ladder right next to the window.

Part of my concern with this homestead is the fact that the main stairway is in continuation with the one into the cellar which is close to the oil burner. In the event that a fire originated in the cellar, the stairwell could act like a chimney. Who wants to descend into a fire in order to escape?

Now, three years later, I feel it prudent to make sure I am still able to perform the "wire act." Katherine stands by to help with the proceedings.

I untangle the chain-link ladder, put it in place, and expect I'll have no trouble crawling out the window and down the ladder. To my consternation I no longer have the strength to swing my left leg out of the window and onto the ladder. With great frustration I try various maneuvers. Finally I give up in exasperation. Katherine helps to rescue me. I am annoyed and humbled. Age has caught up with me! John comments, "I think you had better slow down a bit." Yes, indeed.

Now, of course, a new solution has to be found. Outdoor fire escapes are ugly and become treacherous when laden with ice and snow in winter. Maybe another indoor staircase will have to be devised. This evening I sit down with a pad of paper, ruler, and pencil and I come up with several options which I'm going to present to Jim Moore, my loyal carpenter and renovator of the farm.

Space is limited, so my first choice is either a type of ladder found in a fire station or circular stairs which would fit in the corner at the far end of the guest room. My second idea would be to build a narrow staircase which could be walled off. Option one and two are instantly rejected by Jim as being out of keeping with the 1850 farmhouse. He takes several measurements and tells me he'll be in touch. Within days he arrives with sketches he has made. Little do I know that he copied an old staircase in the home of architect

The new staircase.

Payson Webber, who had taken the design from a period house when he built his home in 1928. This stairway starts like a fan and saves one step. It is the perfect solution. We have half an inch to spare to avoid cutting into the window frame upstairs.

Jim goes to work. Before long we have a safe and handsome staircase with double railings and a door at the top. Jim matches the wall trim and when all is finished the stairs look like part of this old house. The door to the outdoors is within reach. Now if the fire alarm blows, it is only a matter of scooting across to the guest bedroom, down the stairs and out. I've disposed of the chain-link ladder and I'm at ease knowing there is a safe exit from the upstairs.

Snow

November 12, 1996

Nine days ago the farm received the first covering of snow, albeit only an inch or so. The snow remained just a few hours before it melted.

Yesterday—a dark, cold day—the sky was covered by heavy, gray clouds. With temperatures near freezing, it suddenly started to snow while Katherine, Sally, and I had lunch. In no time two inches accumulated. This morning it is truly a winter landscape. It was described as a Currier and Ives print by radio commentator Mark Breen in his "Eye on the Sky" weather report this morning. Sunny breaks during the day are promised. This is a gentle arrival of winter compared to the events in Ohio and the Great Lakes region which received two feet of heavy, wet snow. Massive electrical outing and nine deaths made this a treacherous event. This is five times the average snowfall for November in the Great Lakes region. Vermont is receiving only the tail end of this disaster, making us lucky this time. A Siberian cold front pushed this weather into the states. Maybe the tabloid I saw at the checkout counter in September had some basis for the prediction that this will be the coldest winter in 100 years.

Yesterday I received as a gift from a neighbor a truckload of horse manure for the rose bushes. It will be next week before the roses will get their winter protection. In fact we have already covered our beloved rose plants with hay, ensuring that no serious damage will occur until we complete the distribution of the manure to them.

The water to the barn has been shut off, the woodshed is filled to the brim with dry wood, the snowblower is running smoothly after returning from its checkup, and the larder is filled with staples. We are now ready for winter.

I have also filled the bird feeders with sunflower seed. Already a pair of blue jays and ten or more chickadees have located the source of food. Conspicuously absent are all squirrels. The old apple tree harbors no rodents this fall. I miss the little animals whom I usually see poking out of the old crack in the trunk of the tree to survey the weather before dashing the 30 feet to the bird feeders. It is early though; maybe one or the other pair of squirrels will find the tree before long. On the other hand, the hawks this summer and fall seem to have reduced the squirrel population dramatically. The absence of squirrels will be good for my pocketbook as they eat large amounts of sunflower seed. But the fun I have watching the antics of these smart little animals is worth the cost.

The visits from Green Mountain Bear will come to a close shortly as the snow and cold will put him into a state of pleasant hibernation for several months.

It will be an eventful winter as always, no matter what.

The Ruins

December 17, 1996

Several folks have told me of the doings at the farm during the Civil War. The charcoal furnaces were in full swing. Twenty-four hours a day people were stoking the fires and watching the furnaces. It took two acres of lumber per day to keep them going. The valley was filled with soot and smoke. All this was a war effort. The furnaces at Furnace Brook closed down in 1866. The charcoal went from here on to iron furnaces up the valley to Forestdale. These iron furnaces have been rebuilt and now are an historic site.

Allen Hitchcock, who has a beautiful farm nearby, shares much interest in the history of furnaces. He has given me a book to read, titled *200 Years of Soot and Sweat, The History, Archeology of Vermont Iron, Charcoal and Lime Industries*, by Victor R. Roland. It is a fascinating, detailed description of 19th-Century activity in Vermont, the reference for anyone interested in the subject. Included is a brief description of the charcoal furnaces of this farm.

This leads me to explore the ruins. All we find is shown in the photo. The ruins are located about 1000 feet to the east of River Road and a quarter of a mile north of the homestead. In summer, trees and grass obstruct the view. All iron doors have disappeared. Much charcoal is at the site to attest to the correct location. Red bricks used for the walls of the furnace are strewn all around the foundation. It is a sad sight.

By the end of the Civil War all hillsides of the valley had been lumbered. It is then that Mr. Holden sells off some of the land, keeping the homestead and 104 acres. In time, the trees regrow and are cut at least twice more. The stand of woods at the present is thin and will need several years to reach a size worth lumbering.

Life comes and goes full circle.

The ruins of the charcoal furnace.

Tiger! Tiger! . . . at Mountain Top!

December 18, 1996

November of this year was bitter cold. Icicles formed in Furnace Brook, the temperature hovered around 15 degrees Fahrenheit, and we received an abundance of snow.

Thanksgiving came and went without the visit of Green Mountain Bear. He obviously is hibernating and I feel badly that he did not receive the honey and milk I promised him earlier in the year. Sixteen inches of snow surely is more than he would wish to wade through even for a bowl of his beloved honey.

For the last three days we have had a thaw and much of the ice and snow has disappeared. A gentle rain is falling and melting the snow. The woods look dark and menacing; the brook is running high. The large pine tree near the barn is lit for Christmas early this year to cheer up the dark afternoons and evenings. Walking at dusk I've seen foxes, skunks, and a porcupine near the barn. Hoof marks of deer and moose surround the Christmas tree. I'm wondering what brings the animals into the valley.

As I sit working at my computer, I hear a grunting noise outside the window which announces the presence of an animal. Scratching on the windowpane tells me Green Mountain Bear has come out of hibernation and surely is here to claim his honey.

As I open the window I hear the bear's familiar voice, "I'm back. Will you receive me? Tonight it is dark and wet outdoors."

"You've come for milk and honey?" I inquire.

"Oh, yes, that would be nice, though, to be truthful, a much more serious problem needs your attention."

"A much more serious problem? What's that? Are you or one of your friends injured?" I question the bear.

"Let me tell you what I know. Late November or thereabouts, when it snowed and turned cold, the fox stopped by and called into my den: 'Tiger! Tiger! . . . at Mountain Top!' I was startled, for Mountain Lion is very truthful. The lion was in a hurry. The lion said something about heading toward Furnace Brook and mentioned a lighted Christmas tree at your farm. It made little sense to me. The next day a lynx and a badger came with the same message, 'Tiger! Tiger! . . . at Mountain Top!'

"The following day rain drenched the land. It turned warm and I came out of hibernation. Late afternoon the skunk wanted refuge in my den, proclaiming to be frightened and announcing once again, 'Tiger! Tiger! . . . at Mountain Top!' I was in a fix. The skunk family readily gets nervous and I do not wish to have my nice clean den smelling of skunk all winter. So I informed the skunk to move down to your renovated barn. I explained to the animal that, in my sleep, I could roll over and smother him. Fortunately, the skunk moved on.

"Today, believe it or not, the porcupine arrived at my den with the same message, 'Tiger! Tiger! . . . at Mountain Top!' By now I was mighty curious what this announcement of a tiger at Mountain Top was all about. I beckoned the jays to stop, and I talked to them, asking for an explanation. 'Why are all the animals so agitated and worried? Who is this tiger?'

"The jays returned to tell me that the tiger is a Siberian tiger, weighing 900 pounds and 12 feet in length from nose to tail tip. The jays overheard it said that the tiger is 13 years old, the largest cat in the world. He is stunningly beautiful, though fierce and intimidating. Should I believe any of this? What is a Siberian tiger doing in Vermont at this time of year?"

I replied, "Now, there is a good question. What can I tell you about Siberian tigers? They are an endangered species. It is estimated only 150 to 200 are alive in Siberia. They each require close to 800 square miles of forest for their territory in order to find enough prey to survive in this cold climate. Cutting down the primordial forest of Siberia and the encroachment by man leads to repeated killing of the tiger or the cubs. It is very sad. The Bengal tiger of India is about half the size of the Siberian one. India has set up tiger reserves, though even there the animals are likely to be poached. In India the tigers in the reserves are a major tourist attraction. Bus loads of tourists come to photograph the animals. In the Sundarbans tiger reserve, near the Bangladesh delta, the tigers live in mangrove forests and are man-eating. There the animal is revered and tolerated. Tourists have limited access and the tigers are hard to find in the open. Maybe 200 to 300 live in this region. *Spell of the Tiger,* by Sy Montgomery, tells all about the Sundarbans tigers and the traditions and myths of the region."

"You've gone astray, I think," comes the comment of Green Mountain Bear. "Will you do something to protect all the animals that have come to the farm in fear and desperation? Will you go and inquire about this Siberian tiger? Have you ever seen such a tiger? Will you take your camera? Are you afraid of a tiger?" Green Mountain Bear besieges me with questions.

"Now, slow down just a might! You sure are full of questions and concerns this evening."

"That's to be expected. A Siberian tiger in Vermont, if it is true, is a most extraordinary event. Are you not excited?"

"Should I be?" I inquire. "I'm not sure any of what you tell me can be believed."

"You have always trusted the jays and me, have you not?"

"Maybe the jays have sighted the tiger, but as for you, my friend, what you have told me is only hearsay. Your testimony would not stand up in a court of law. Are you sure you did not make up this story? Were you frightened when I told you about Shere Kahn the tiger in Rudyard Kipling's *Jungle Book?*"

"No such thing. After all, I live in Vermont where there were no tigers until this Siberian tiger showed up."

"You have not seen this animal, have you?"

"No, but my den is very close to Mountain Top. I've heard some terrible roaring. This may have been the tiger for all I know."

"Did any of the animals which told you 'Tiger! Tiger! . . . at Mountain Top' give you any details?"

"No, they were in too great a hurry to put distance between the tiger and themselves. Most are settled near your barn and near the lighted Christmas tree. Should I have some of them come to the window and then you can ask them yourself?"

"That won't be necessary," I replied.

"When Santa Claus and the reindeer stop this Christmas Eve I'll inquire about matters. Santa Claus is one of the best informed in this world."

"Do you light the tree outdoors as a beacon of light for Santa Claus and the reindeer? Are they likely to lose their way traveling from city to city, and from continent to continent?"

"I'm sure they can find their way. On the other hand, lighting the tree is a gracious thing to do—

sort of giving a helping hand. Then, too, all animals know they may spend the night near the tree without fear of attack from a predator. It is a rule as old as the one that states that during a severe drought all animals are safe at the watering hole. It is a place to take respite. This year there are a few bales of hay in the barn for the reindeer. If hay is left over, the moose and deer can help themselves to the remaining hay. In any event, it makes good bedding for the little animals."

"Talking about sustenance, is it not time for my honey and milk before I return to the forest and my den?"

Green Mountain Bear has not forgotten our agreement. The beehives have been undisturbed—the bear is entitled to his reward.

I return with a dish of honey and milk. The bear laps up his treat in a hurry, grunting with delight. Then, true to form, he is off into the woods, relieved that I'll take care and inquire about the Siberian tiger.

Was he worried about the Siberian tiger? It is for certain that he was perplexed and indignant at the intrusion of a stranger.

The next morning paw imprints are all around the Christmas tree, though, by daylight the animals have left the yard to go off and forage. Last night Santa Claus did not stop off with his reindeer, though soon enough I'll hear the sleigh bells in my sleep.

Now, about the Siberian tiger. I drove to Mountain Top and found the tiger fenced in a wooded area. Wildlife photographers were busily at work. The tiger had come for a brief visit from a game farm in Montana. Several other animals, such as the Arctic fox, wolf, and leopard had come along, as well as a grizzly bear and black bear. I've been privileged to document their presence with the camera. I'm sure the bear will ask to see the photos of the Siberian tiger in spring when he comes out of hibernation. I surely do not wish to disappoint my friend.

As for Santa Claus, he did stop by on Christmas eve. The bells of the reindeer woke me just past midnight. It brought back glorious memories of childhood.

"Merry Christmas to all and may the Siberian tiger and other Arctic animals survive for many more centuries." This message I pinned to the lighted tree. Santa Claus picked up the note that night. Thus, all is well. "Happy New Year and good health to all!"

The Siberian Tiger,
much feared by all others in the animal kingdom.

The grisly bear, visitor to Vermont.

The Arctic leopard, another visitor.

The mountain lion, rarely seen in Vermont.

The Arctic fox, a visitor from the far north.

The red fox, native to Vermont.

The badger, another local inhabitant.

The fisher, a ferocious hunter of porcupine, is a rarely-seen resident of Vermont.

The skunk, a well-established and often-seen inhabitant of Vermont. (An animal best left to itself!)

The lynx, a native to this state.

The Arctic wolf, a visitor far from home.

*The Otter, seen along Furnace Brook
and throughout Vermont*

The porcupine, reintroduced to Vermont,
is now well at home in the state.

A Letter to Santa Claus

December 20, 1996

Each year, usually starting in November, Santa Claus receives hundreds of letters from the children of the world. Some ask for toys, some for books. Others who are more needy ask for clothes and food. The list of items requested seems endless. Santa Claus and his helpers try to deliver all things asked for. There is always a last-minute rush even though preparation for Christmas starts in January and lasts all year.

One year there was a shortage of cabbage patch dolls; another year there were hardly enough skateboards to go around. Warm, woolly clothes and sturdy winter boots are much in demand. There are never quite enough gingerbread cookies. The grownups, remembering their own childhood, help themselves to many gingerbread cookies no matter how many are delivered. An occasional youngster will go without! One year, Santa Claus had only one gingerbread cookie per family. It was a year when war was raging over in Europe. Due to the air attacks and exploding bombs, Santa Claus limited his deliveries. He was afraid the reindeer herd would come to harm and it would take many years to replace the animals. It was a year with no true Christmas spirit. Mail delivery was interrupted and he was very, very sad. That was a long time ago, before today's children were born.

Santa Claus reads all of the children's letters. He has a pile for each request. One pile is for dolls and one for bicycles, as well one each for sleds, soldiers, castles, musical instruments, and the like. He is disappointed when the letters only say "Bring me . . ." or "I want . . ." He recalls with delight a letter that read:

Dear Santa:
Please remember me, and if you have a dollhouse left over, I would love one very much. If you can spare the parts, I'll try to build it myself. I would like the dollhouse for my little sister. I know you are so very busy.
Thank you very much . . .

After Christmas he especially enjoys a "Thank You" note, though, as a rule, there are not many.

This year Santa found a special letter pinned to the Christmas tree at Furnace Brook Farm. It read:

Dear Santa:
Could you possibly help? I live near a zoo. On my way to school I pass by all the zoo animals. They look so sad and seem so homesick it makes me cry. Could you free them this Christmas? Would you take the polar bear north to the Arctic, and the elephant, the lions, the zebra, the wildbeast and the gnu home to the Kalahari of Africa? The tiger came from India, a different continent! The tropical birds, for the most part, will fly to

South America. The buffalo and eagles belong in Yellowstone Park. Oh, don't forget the kangaroo and koala bear! I know it is a long way to Australia but that is where their companions are. The pandas would much prefer to be home in China. The climate here does not seem to agree with them. My only wish is to free the animals and return them to their companions in the wild. I think you are the only one left to help the zoo animals escape to their homes. Thank you for reading my letter.

Much love, and Merry Christmas . . .

"Hmm," exclaimed Santa Claus, "I have never thought about this. The little girl might be right. The zoo animals do look sad and lonesome. They don't understand why man has taken their freedom and put them behind bars. Who will free them if I and my helpers don't return them to their native countries? Oh, dear, that will be quite a project—a major undertaking! The elephant is so large, an especially large sleigh will have to be built for him and it may require an extra team of reindeer to pull the sleigh. We could try to use a pair of elephants as a team but they are so weakened from lack of exercise it is unlikely we would get very far."

The more Santa thought about the problem the more he became intrigued by the idea of freeing all the zoo animals. Most birds could fly home by themselves, though there were some whose wings had been clipped. These birds would need transportation. All the sleighs will need to be painted with their destination: Africa, Australia, India, China, South America, Arctic and Antarctica, so as to make sure no animal gets lost.

But then, what about all the empty zoos? Would that bring sadness to some children who did not recognize that zoos are prisons? "I will have to think about this and perhaps consult with Mrs. Santa Claus and all my helpers." he reasoned.

A winter garden of icicles on Santa's window.

Could zoos be used as a playground for children? No, that would not be welcome. Nobody likes to be behind bars!

A dark-haired elf speaks up, "I have a solution. Let's fill the zoos with stuffed animals. Imagine all the fun we will have sewing soft, huggable animals, such as giraffes, lions, rabbits, and even crocodiles." Another elf joins in, saying, "We could furnish all zoos with the glorious nature films showing the animals in their own habitat."

Santa Claus muses, "It may take some time for me to plan and organize this venture but one of these Christmases I will reward the little girl for being so thoughtful about animals.

This is a special letter–a real challenge–thought Santa Claus. He is delighted in anticipating the joy of all the zoo animals and of the children when they realize what it means to the animals to live free again. The animals will be grateful for the rest of time.

Merry Christmas to all creatures big and small!

Another Visit from the Bear

December 24, 1996

Yesterday it looked like it was going to be a white Christmas. Today it is another matter. Rain is drenching the land. The temperature is up to 40 degrees Fahrenheit and the roads are icy. The valley is fogged in and Furnace Brook has risen and is quite noisy. We are experiencing another unexpected winter thaw. The grays prevail from light to dark with the bark on the trees being nearly black. There are no birds nor squirrels in sight. It is simply too wet.

At the edge of the homestead I see the footprints of a bear. Probably Green Mountain Bear came calling last evening when I was in Rutland. He will be indignant to have ventured out of his den only to find no one home.

Darkness is settling in early today, enhanced by the low, dense cloud cover and mist and fog over the land. I'm reflecting upon the year past, only to be interrupted by tapping on the window. So, the bear is back.

"Are you there, Green Mountain Bear?" I inquire as I open the window.

"Yes, I saw the smoke rising from the chimney so I figured you were here."

"You're quite correct. What's on your mind to bring you into the valley this evening?"

"Just came for a visit. Last evening you were away," he replies.

"I saw your tracks by the house."

"I should have known you were in town because none of the chimneys smoked, at least that was my conclusion. I wanted company so I went south to see if Katherine was home. I've always wanted to visit with her Celtic Bear, the one who has a large basketball. I thought that would be fun."

"So how did you make out?" I coax the bear into telling of his adventure.

"I didn't make out," he says with disappointment.

Green Mountain Bear coming for a visit.

"You didn't? That's strange."

"Well, let me tell you what happened. When I entered Katherine's driveway, bright lights came on. These frightened me. I then approached her house through the woods. I saw lights were on in the house, but all blinds were drawn. I listened and could not make out what the conversation was all about."

"Was it possibly a Celtic's game on television?" I suggest.

"Might have been for all I know. There were moments of loud noise. I never could understand the announcer if there was one. I tapped on the windows but nobody responded. Not even the Celtic Bear; he should have recognized a bear tap. He was either sound asleep or totally engrossed by the basketball game he was watching."

"What about Katherine? Didn't she look out the window to see what the noise was all about?"

"No! And, you know, I even tapped vigorously." he asserts.

"Did you really?"

"Yes, yes, I really did. Then, again, I did not wish to break a windowpane and frighten Katherine. I did want to be polite."

"So, what did you do then? Did you get a glimpse of Celtic Bear?"

"Not even that. I waited a while and then came back up along Furnace Brook to the farm. Then I returned to my den ever so disappointed."

"So, that is why you came moseying about this evening?" I finally surmise.

"Well, I suppose so. After all, I am here," he replies assertively.

"Do you know it will be Christmas Eve in a little while?"

"There is talk about Christmas Eve among all the animals. Of course I know that."

"Well, then, Merry Christmas, my little friend!"

"Merry Christmas to you and to all who love the farm and who are kind and gentle to the animals. I must remind you though, I'm no longer little. Even my den will be a bit tight this winter as I've grown so much this summer."

"Oh, I was probably patronizing. No harm meant, Green Mountain Bear. Is there anything else on your mind this evening?"

"Yes, I have a question you may be able to answer."

"What's your question?"

"When will my beloved have the cubs? And when will I be able to see and play with the cubs?"

"Dear me, that is not an easy question. I can't be sure. I have a hunch you will have to wait until spring—around maple sugaring time or thereabout. Don't you remember I told you last spring that if mother is very protective she may not allow you or any other bear to come close. You may be able to get a glimpse, but to play with the cubs . . . I doubt mother bear will permit this. It has nothing to do with you. You must not take this personal as it is the instinct of a mother to protect her cubs and defend them fiercely."

"Hmm, I guess I do remember you warning me of this before."

Green Mountain Bear seems sad this evening. Maybe I can take his mind off his cubs and his beloved. "The young family will be fine. In time, when mother feels secure, she most likely will bring the cubs to see you. Now, I have a question for you, Green Mountain Bear."

"You do?" the bear asks with surprise.

"A little while ago I heard you say, 'Yes, yes.' From whom did you pick up the double positive? Double negatives are prevalent in many languages, but hardly ever a double positive."

"I learned it from you."

"Did you really? Let's be truthful."

"Well, maybe I say it in moments of exuberance. I've never really thought about it," comes his reply.

"To be honest, I've never really thought about it either. Everyone I question claims they also have picked up 'yes, yes' from me. I thought you, Green Mountain Bear, might have coined this expletive. Don't you want to take credit?"

"Hmm, should I? Would it help you?"

"It might. But then who would give a bear this much credit? People would make fun of me if I invoked you as the originator of 'yes, yes.'"

"How about crediting Emily Dickinson? You quoted her on the last page of your *Wild Oats* book."

"That probably would be met with disbelief and I could not substantiate this claim."

"Then it is you after all?"

"I suppose so," I admit.

"Yes, yes, it is you! I'll tell the other animals. Merry Christmas! Evening has arrived. Yes, yes, I'll be on my way now."

"Wait a minute. I have a Christmas treat for you."

"How thoughtful! What is it? Honey and milk?" the bear asks expectantly.

"It is something special . . . a bag of marshmallows. You can enjoy these in your den before you go off to sleep for the next few months."

"Thank you. Remember, if we get a January or February thaw I'll come to visit you, no doubt. Yes, yes, you'll be lonesome if I don't come around to see you from time to time, weather permitting. This is my Christmas gift to you—it is a promise which I will keep. You can depend on it."

"Oh, that would be nice of you. Thank you, Green Mountain Bear."

Clutching the bag of marshmallows the bear scampers off into the fog-shrouded woods.

Yes, yes, it is Christmas.

Fog and Rain

December 29, 1996

This truly has been a stark Christmas. All snow has melted and we have had a substantial amount of rain and fog and very few sunny days to cheer us up. Today in the early afternoon the fog is dense around the farm. The barn can hardly be discerned and the woods are thick with fog.

I detect a dark figure coming out of the woods, rotund and low slung, with a lumbering gait. It must be Green Mountain Bear on a stroll. I'm not surprised that the bear makes a bee line toward my den. What could be on his mind today? It won't take long for him to confide in me. By now he trusts me and finds a good outlet in telling me about his woes and worries. The bear slows and sniffs the air. He will not be disappointed. A warm fire gives off a pungent odor of burning maple wood. The smoke does not rise and mixes with the fog, which makes for even poorer visibility. In expectation I open the den window and quietly wait for a grunt or for the bear's approach.

In a cautious, nearly subdued voice, a murmured "I'm here," informs me Green Mountain Bear has arrived.

I greet him with my usual, "Welcome!"

"Am I interrupting you?" Green Mountain Bear asks somewhat timidly.

"Maybe a little . . I'm at the computer, as you can see."

"Can your writing wait a bit? I'd like to talk to you. I have news from other animals."

"So, today you are a messenger for the inhabitants of the forest?"

"Sort of. The others are too timid to come to you for conversation. I am not afraid to chat with you most any time as long as it is safe for me to return to my den without harm."

"I know what you mean. Now what is the news?" I inquire.

"The fox, mountain lion, lynx, badger, skunk, and even the porcupine are delighted they were able to take refuge near your lighted Christmas tree. They are all overjoyed the Siberian tiger has left Vermont. Most of them have either denned up for winter or gone their way. They saw you turn off the Christmas tree lights and they got the message. They did not harm each other. The animals want you to know they even had a chance to see the reindeer and Santa Claus. By the way, Santa Claus found the note that you pinned to the Christmas tree and he put it into his mail pouch.

"In spite of all that has happened, the animals are too shy to allow you to take photographs. They will move fast if they see you approach with a camera in hand. They all wish you a 'Happy New Year,' and hope you will continue to be spokesperson for their welfare. And of course I join in too. After all, I am one of them." There is a pause. Then Green Mountain Bear continues,

"Have you heard if the Siberian tiger will be back next year?"

"I really don't know for sure. It is too early to be certain. If I learn the tiger is coming, I'll let you know."

"We'll know soon enough, as his roar is unmistakable and it penetrates the woods like the warning of a fog horn. Fear will strike and word of his presence will spread through the valley like wildfire."

"You sound as relieved at the tiger's departure as the jungle was when Shere Kahn, the Bengal tiger in Kipling's *Jungle Book*, is trampled to death by the buffalo herd," I remark.

"Fear is terrible—you know that."

"Yes, I know fear is terrible, though on occasion it is essential for survival," I explain.

"When did fear come to you?"

"Never mind . . . that's discussion for another time."

For a moment the bear and I seem buried in our own thoughts, then Green Mountain Bear resumes the conversation. "One more question before I depart. You wouldn't have another bag of marshmallows for me to take along?"

"A bag of marshmallows? Maybe. Let me go and look in the kitchen."

"Here," I present Green Mountain Bear with a partially filled bag of marshmallows, "these will have to do for the moment. They are all I have."

"Oh, thanks, this will be a delicate treat to have on hand. So you enjoy marshmallows too? They are not only for me?"

"Quite so," I respond, as the bear reaches for his treat. Then, grasping the bag, he heads up the mountain without another word.

"Happy New Year and a good spell of peaceful hibernation," I call after my friend.

I'm wondering when the cold will set in to keep the bear curled up for the next few months. New Year 1997 is on the horizon and the imminent change of weather to bitter cold can't be far away. Lost in my thoughts, I close the window to keep the damp out of the house. I'll miss the company of the bear on dark evenings. But before I know it, he'll show up with the onset of maple sugaring, thin and hungry and full of questions. Sweet dreams, little bear!

Ice in Furnace Brook in January.

The New Year

January 16, 1997

The new year is in full swing. The days are getting longer, winter storms are plaguing the nation, to which Vermont is no exception. Rain, sleet, snow, and slush were my companions on my way out to the farm. It would have been more sensible to stay in Rutland. Restlessness and the need to make sure the farm was still here became the explanation that I offered to concerned friends. The dark gray sky with low cloud cover seemed to fit my mood. The wet, dark trees and the solitude of the farm always says something special to me. The brook today is more subdued than I expected.

Then I observe a quite unexpected surprise. Sixteen goldfinches are occupying all rungs of the two tubular bird feeders filled with thistle seed. A full house! This is a first since hanging the feeders at Thanksgiving. Today there is no sight of the large red-shouldered hawk. This bird has been patrolling the valley in wide circles looking for prey. It is a gorgeous sight to behold as long as one does not think of the wee animals whose life is forfeited for the hawk's existence. This chain of events throughout nature is part of the essence of life.

Suddenly I am interrupted by a noise by my window as I hear grunting and scratching at the windowsill. The dark figure leaves no doubt it is Green Mountain Bear.

119

"What brings you around in the twilight of the day?" I inquire.

"I've got to talk to you," my bear friend responds urgently. In this fickle winter weather, warm one day, cold the next, I can't get into a good sound sleep. This morning I awoke terribly hungry. There are no grubs beneath the tree bark that I explored so I decided to go for a fish in the brook. I had no luck. The fish are in hiding for the winter, I suppose. I ended up cold and wet. Then in the glistening of the rain I see a two-foot

Green Mountain Bear ends up cold and wet.

fish lying on one of the rocks near the brook. I lurched for it. You won't believe me, I'm afraid, but there wasn't any fish on the rock, though from a distance I could swear it was a large fish. So I need an explanation . . . and I very much would like a decent meal, not just marshmallows—even though they are delicious, they are not very filling."

"Well, that is quite a story," I remarked. "While we talk, I'll defrost some frozen fish for you. This will have to do. I'm not supplied with much bear food, I regret to say."

"That would be very nice! I'm so hungry I'm not fussy. You know what I mean!"

"Now as to the rock with the image of a fish on it. I know that rock as well as several others. These rocks are marked with fish imprints which are the residue of fossils deposited thousands of years ago."

"You'll have to explain to me what fossils are. Are they bear traps of sort? You have no idea how perplexed and disappointed I am. How can nature make such a fool of me? I believe I heard the jays chuckle when I came up empty-handed. I don't consider this to be funny, not when I am as hungry as I am."

"If you will quiet down a bit, I'll try and explain. The study of fossils is called 'paleontology.'"

"Paleontology is just another useless word to me," the bear interjects, mildly annoyed. "It does not explain a thing. You do clutter things up, don't you?"

"Now, hold your horses—or whatever. You can't be so impatient—even on an empty stomach," I reply while I mull over the shortest, simplest explanation to give a hungry young bear. "Fossils are remnants of plants or animals which lived thousands of years ago and became preserved in the earth's crust. They became embedded in rock such as shale, limestone, or some other geological element. A fossil imprint occurs when the petrified skeletal remains leave behind the shape of the plant or animal. You saw the perfect imprint of a fish, which is especially noticeable after a rain in glistening light."

"So I was fooled by a false image?"

"Fossil imprints are very real images of things gone by."

"A historical record?"

"Exactly," I reply, "I think you have grasped the concept."

"Will I turn into a fossil some day?" the bear queries.

"It is possible, though unlikely I'd say."

"Are there many fossil imprints on this farm to fool unsuspecting animals like me for instance?"

"From now on you no longer will be fooled. There are plenty of fossil imprints if you make up your mind to examine rocks carefully."

"Have you taken any photos of these imprints?"

"Yes, I have a few photos—nothing very spectacular. I recently read that in 1864 the fossil of an elephant was discovered in Mount Holly, about thirty miles from here. That was an important discovery which is recorded in the Rutland Directory of the time. This book also mentions fossils that are located near Furnace Brook."

"So you know all about such matters?" the bear follows up our conversation.

"I know a little. It is a field of study to occupy a lifetime if one is so inclined."

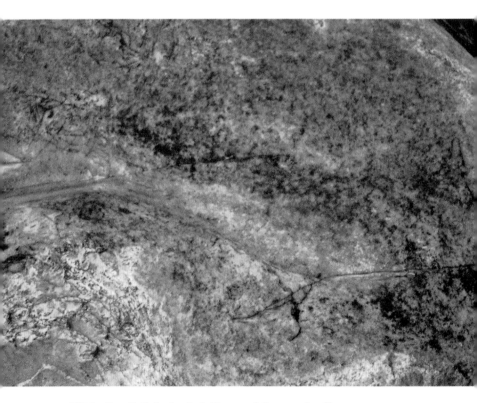

This fossil fish fooled Green Mountain Bear.

"Are you so inclined?"

"Not really. I lack patience and persistence."

"Well, yes, you are human, as you remind me on occasion."

The bear seems satisfied for the moment. I fetch the defrosted fish out of the microwave oven and present my friend with a plate of food to still his appetite. It is about time to turn cold and stay cold. We are having a fickle winter so far. In Vermont it is unlikely the mild weather will last for long. If the weather pattern does not change I may have to put in some emergency supplies of winter bear food. I have no doubt it is slim-pickings for a bear in January. I realize that I cannot abandon my friend Green Mountain Bear now.

Time is too slow for those who wait,
Too swift for those who fear,
Too long for those who grieve,
Too short for those who rejoice;
But for those who love, time is eternity.

– Henry Van Dyke

A place to bear your own thoughts . . .